Alfred Werner (1866—1919)

George B. Kauffman , 1930

Alfred Werner, 1866 - 1919

Founder of Coordination Chemistry

Springer-Verlag Berlin Heidelberg New York 1966

Dr. GEORGE B. KAUFFMAN
Professor of Chemistry
California State College, Fresno, California, USA

Die Chemie muss zur Astronomie der Molekularwelt werden.

A. Werner

Autograph quotation "Chemistry must become the astronomy of the molecular world" from "Handschriften zeitgenössischer Chemiker, gesammelt für die Damenspende des Chemikerkränzchens", 1905

To Dr. Louis C. W. Baker,

who as a young and patient instructor of freshman chemistry at the University of Pennsylvania, once took the time and effort to initiate the author into the amazing mysteries of the octahedron and so demonstrated to him that the carbon atom possesses no monopoly on stereochemistry.

Lou Baker received his doctorate under Prof. Thomas P. McCutcheon, who had worked with Werner in Zürich. Thus, the author is pleased to claim a direct, even if highly tenuous, academic link with the Master.

Foreword

A generation ago, nearly all college students who planned to become chemists were required to take a course in the history of their subject, but nowadays, such courses are usually not required, and in many schools, are not even offered. It is argued that the subject of chemistry is expanding so rapidly that students can hardly master the material which fills the new text books, to say nothing of learning what chemists thought and did a century ago. Although this point of view has some validity, it fails to take into account the much more important fact that one cannot really understand or appreciate the present position of science unless he knows something of the slow and tortuous steps through which it developed. His ability to help it move forward will be greatly enhanced by an understanding of the thinking of the chemists who built the theories which we use today. It has been truly said, "He who knows only his own generation remains always a child."

The appearance of a book which details the birth of a great development in chemistry is therefore a significant event, and one which we welcome warmly. The events which are chronicled here are now far enough behind us to allow a clear evaluation of their significance, but close enough that there still remain a few people who knew WERNER personally, and who have preserved intimate records of his work. Thus, Prof. KAUFFMAN has undertaken the task of writing this book at a most propitious time. In compiling this work, he has drawn upon his extensive background in inorganic chemistry and his long standing interest in the history of science and has produced a book which is both authoritative and highly readable. We are all in his debt.

University of Illinois   JOHN C. BAILAR, JR.
Urbana, Illinois

Preface and Acknowledgments

It was with much trepidation that I undertook the present study of ALFRED
WERNER. The great scientific biographies of the past such as ERNST COHEN's
study of JACOBUS HENRICUS VAN'T HOFF (1912) or RICHARD MEYER's biography
of his brother VICTOR MEYER (1917) continually served to remind me of the many
difficulties inherent in the task. I could not muster nearly the quantity of material available to these other biographers. WERNER's laboratory notebooks had
unfortunately not been preserved. With a few exceptions, a complete file of
extant letters was available only for the years 1896—1904 and 1907—1909. In
most cases, the replies of WERNER's correspondents had not been preserved. Moreover, I was not close to my subject, either in age, environment, or nationality.
I hope that my experience and abiding interest in coordination chemistry and the
history of chemistry have partially helped to overcome these handicaps.
My original sources consisted mainly of letters, lecture notes, administrative
records, dissertations, newspaper articles, and, of course, publications from the
chemical literature. Furthermore, I was highly dependent upon correspondence
and interviews with persons who had worked with WERNER, had attended his
lectures, or were otherwise acquainted with him professionally or socially. In
an attempt to recapture WERNER's *milieu,* whenever possible I made it a point
to visit the places where he had lived and worked.
This book thus includes considerable unpublished biographical data and illustrations. It was my goal to present an objective portrait of WERNER as a man,
teacher, and scientist. I am acutely aware of the lack of definition in the portrait
which emerges. ALFRED WERNER's personality was as complex as that of the compounds on which he worked, and inconsistencies both in oral and written testimony were many. When I made use of rumors or conjectural stories, the fact
that such anecdotes are merely speculative has, I hope, been clearly indicated.
Even the casual reader may miss the familiar octahedron, so inseparably linked
with WERNER and coordination chemistry. However, my deliberate decision to
limit myself in this brief volume to a non-technical portrait of WERNER and
his times has a twofold basis. First, I hope that such a primarily non-chemical
study of WERNER's life will be found useful, especially by the general reader

with only a passing interest in coordination chemistry. In this book, therefore, technical details are not permitted to intrude upon personal and chronological events. Second, I do not wish to duplicate the material to be contained in the extensive critical analysis of WERNER's thought, achievements, and their far-reaching influence, on which I am currently working. For comprehensive details, then, the reader is referred to my recent translation into English of WERNER's major works ("Classics in Coordination Chemistry: Part I. The Selected Papers of Alfred Werner," Dover Publications, Inc., New York, **1966**), the General Bibliography at the end of the present volume, and the above-mentioned forthcoming study.

And now for the pleasant task of acknowledging those who assisted in this study.

This investigation could not have been made without the generous financial assistance of both the History and Philosophy of Science Program, Social Sciences Division, National Science Foundation (Grant GS-74) and of the American Philosophical Society (Grant 3255, Penrose Fund), which made possible my year's study of WERNER's life and work at Universität Zürich. Thanks are also due to the California State College at Fresno for awarding me a leave of absence. I further wish to express my gratitude to Fräulein CHARLOTTE WERNER of Zürich for graciously making available her father's papers, notes, and photographs. Without her cooperation, this book would never have materialized.

I am also indebted to Prof. ERNST SCHUMACHER, former Direktor, Anorganisch-Chemisches Institut der Universität Zürich, and Prof. GEROLD SCHWARZENBACH, Direktor, Laboratorium für Anorganische Chemie, Eidgenössische Technische Hochschule. In numerous helpful discussions, these gentlemen not only provided many significant facts about WERNER's life and work but also made a visiting scholar feel at home in a foreign country.

Frau Dr. ANNA ELISABETH ERNST (née DORN) of Kressbronn am Bodensee deserves my special thanks. This indomitable octogenarian, endowed with the enthusiasm and energy usually reserved for persons one-fourth her age, received her doctorate under WERNER over sixty years ago and has devoted many years to collecting material for a biography of her beloved former teacher. Despite illnesses and accidents, she never failed to respond to my numerous pleas for information and advice.

I am also obligated to WERNER's successor at Universität Zürich, Prof. emeritus PAUL KARRER, who has done more than anyone else to preserve WERNER's memory and to publicize his accomplishments. The articles of Prof. KARRER, along with those of PAUL PFEIFFER and ROBERT HUBER, provide an invaluable and insightful introduction to WERNER's life and work, and I have made frequent reference to them in the preparation of this book. JOHN READ's "Humour and Humanism in Chemistry" furnished valuable background material on life in WERNER's institute at the turn of the century.

My thanks also go to Frau FANNY AMEND-WERNER of Baden-Baden, who gave most generously of her time in conducting me on a guided tour of WERNER dwellings in Mulhouse. Other members of the WERNER family who were consulted, particularly regarding genealogical matters, include Prof. ROGER GUY WERNER of the Université de Nancy and the recently deceased Prof. GEORGES HUGEL of the Université de Strasbourg.

It is also my great pleasure to acknowledge the contributions of the following individuals whose names are arranged alphabetically according to country (Former students, Doktoranden, assistants, or co-workers of WERNER are designated with an asterisk.): Denmark: Copenhagen — Prof. JANNIK BJERRUM; England: Birmingham — Prof. J. A. NEWTON FRIEND; Cambridge — Prof. F. G. MANN; Sussex — Prof. T. S. MOORE; France: Mulhouse — Prof. A. BANDERET, M. E. BANNWARTH, Mlle. ELISABETH MATHEY, M. D. MAY, Prof. J. MEYBECK, and Père SIMON; Paris — Profs. MARCEL BATAILLON, MICHAEL BIGORGNE, and MARCEL DELÉPINE; Germany: Bonn — Fräulein CRESCENTIA RODER; Freiburg im Breisgau — the late Prof. HERMANN STAUDINGER; Karlsruhe — Prof. OEHME and R. SCHOLDER; Leipzig — Dr. IRENE STRUBE; Marburg/Lahn — Frau SUSANNE LÖHLEIN (née HANTZSCH); Würzburg — Profs. GÜNTHER BRIEGLEB, BRUNO EMMERT, and F. SOMMER; Italy: Bologna — Prof. GIOVANNI SEMERANO; Genoa — Dr. REINHOLD BÜHLER *; Milan — Dott. ALESSANDRO DELL'AGNOLA; Rome — Dottori FERRUCCIO APRILE and FRANCO ROSSI; Japan: Tokyo — Profs. YUJI SHIBATA * and TAKU UEMURA; Scotland: St. Andrews — the late Prof. JOHN READ *; Sweden: Lund — Prof. STEN AHRLAND; Stockholm — Profs. ULF S. VON EULER, LARS GUNNAR SILLÉN, and ARNE WESTGREN; Uppsala — Prof. ARNE TISELIUS; Switzerland: Basel — Dr. CHARLES GRÄNACHER *, Prof. FRANZ GRÜN, Drs. EMIL LÜSCHER * and HERMANN STAHEL *, Prof. ARTHUR STOLL and ROBERT WIZINGER; Geneva — Dr. CHRISTIAN KLIXBÜLL JØRGENSEN; Glarus — Drs. FERDINAND BLUMER * and AEGIDIUS TSCHUDI *; Zürich — Prof. ERWIN H. ACKERKNECHT, Dr. CARL A. AGTHE *, Prof. AMBROSIUS A. VON ALBERTINI, Frau

A. Blass-Laufer, Profs. Karl Dürr, Alfred Ernst, Hans Fischer*, Kurt Grob, and Arthur Grumbach*, Dr. Hans Hürlimann*, Prof. Johann Jakob*, Herr Jean-Pierre Leuenberger, Prof. Leopold Ruzicka, Dr. Volkemar Scheu*, Profs. Hans Rudolf Schinz*, Otto Schlagenhaufen, E. Schmid, Walter Schneider, and Fritz Schwarz, Herr Ernst Spillmann, and Dr. Hugo Wyler; U.S.A.: Ann Arbor, Mich. — Prof. Kasimir Fajans; Cambridge, Mass. — Prof. Werner Stumm; Durham, N. H. — Prof. Robert E. Lyle; Fresno, Calif. — Drs. Alan D. Button and Raymund F. Wood; Ithaca, N.Y. — Prof. Peter Debye; Los Angeles, Calif. — Prof. Karol Mysels and Dr. Dora Stern*; New Brunswick, N.J. — Dr. Erwin Kuh; Plainfield, N.J. — Mr. Victor R. King; San Francisco, Calif. — Prof. Henry M. Leicester; Stanford, Calif. — Mrs. F. Furst; Urbana, Ill. — Prof. John C. Bailar, Jr.; U.S.S.R.: Kishinev — Dr. M. L. Spritsman*; Leningrad — Akademik A. A. Grinberg; Moscow — Prof. G. V. Bykov, Akademik I. I. Chernyaev, and Dr. Yuri Ivanovich Solov'ev.

I am also happy to acknowledge the assistance of the following organizations and societies: England: London — The Chemical Society; France: Mulhouse — Mairie, Bibliothèque Municipale, and Société Industrielle de Mulhouse; Germany: Bonn — Gesellschaft Deutscher Naturforscher und Ärzte; Braunschweig — Verlag Friedrich Vieweg und Sohn; Frankfurt am Main — Gesellschaft Deutscher Chemiker; Jena — Verlag Gustav Fischer; Karlsruhe — Badisches Generallandesarchiv; Munich — Deutsches Museum; Switzerland: Zürich — Corporationenverband Zürich, Direktion des Innern des Kantons Zürich, Generalkonsulat der Bundesrepublik Deutschland, Gesellschaft Ehemaliger Studierender der ETH, Kanzlei des Schweizerischen Schulrates, Photodruck + Copie AG, Schachgesellschaft Zürich, Seeclub Zürich, Staatsarchiv Zürich, Stadthaus Archiv Zürich, Stella Turicensis, Verband der Studierenden an der ETH, and Vereinigung der Chemiestudierenden an der ETH; U.S.A.: Fresno, Calif. — Calif. State College Library; Philadelphia, Penna. — Academy of Natural Sciences and the Edgar Fahs Smith Memorial Collection in the History of Chemistry.

To Fräulein Liselotte Guyer, Sekretärin, Anorganisch-Chemisches Institut der Universität Zürich, go my heartfelt thanks for services beyond the call of duty in typing the dozens and dozens of letters involved in arranging for interviews or acquiring information. For similar services in the U.S., I am indebted to Mrs. Joyce Stafford, secretary of the California State College at Fresno, Department of Chemistry. I also wish to thank the Research Committee of the California State College at Fresno for a National Science Foundation Institutional Grant which provided funds for typing the manuscript.

Most of the illustrations and all of the manuscripts reproduced in the book were kindly provided by Fräulein CHARLOTTE WERNER. Except for the Frontispiece and Plate 1, none of these, to the best of my knowledge, has ever been published. I am indebted to Fräulein WERNER for all illustrations, with the exceptions now noted: Cover — The WERNER family crest *(Familienwappen)*, compiled from old documents by GEORGE-LÉONARD WERNER, former archivist of the city of Mulhouse — Prof. ROGER GUY WERNER; Plate 5 — Fräulein CRESCENTIA RODER; Plate 8 — Frau SUSANNE LÖHLEIN (née HANTZSCH); Plate 1 — "75 Jahre chemischer Forschung an der Universität Zürich" (Reference 2); Plate 2 — Photograph taken by Prof. PAUL KARRER, courtesy of Dr. AEGIDIUS TSCHUDI.

For his assistance, cooperation, and continual encouragement, I am pleased to recognize Dr. KONRAD F. SPRINGER of Springer-Verlag, Heidelberg. For proofreading the manuscript, I am indebted to TOM BROOKS of the Fresno County Free Library. Any errors, of course, are exclusively mine.

I also wish to thank my family for their patience during the trying ordeal of composition. I am deeply indebted to my wife INGE for her unfailing support as well as for her active participation in this venture as interpreter, translator, and editorial assistant. Finally, to my daughters RUTH and JUDITH, a word of apology for the many occasions on which I was forced to neglect them while working on this book.

G. B. K.

Fresno, California
May, 1966

Contents

XV

Introduction

Occasionally, a single man may play such a central role in a particular field of science that his name becomes synonymous with that field. ALFRED WERNER, the undisputed founder and systematizer of coordination chemistry, is just such a man. Even today, almost a full half-century after his death, coordination compounds, particularly metal-ammines, are still known as WERNER complexes, and the coordination theory is colloquially called WERNER's theory.

At the time of its proposal in 1893 by a twenty-six-year-old *Privat-Dozent,* this revolutionary theory rested upon a minimum of experimental data. WERNER devoted his entire scientific career to the amassing of the experimental evidence required to prove the validity of his youthful assumptions. Beginning with a study of the hitherto unexplained "molecular compounds" (metal-ammines, hydrates, and double salts), his ideas soon encompassed almost the whole of systematic inorganic chemistry and also found application in the organic area. His experimental and theoretical papers remain even today a foundation and guide for investigations in coordination chemistry. He was the first to demonstrate that stereochemistry is a general phenomenon not limited to carbon compounds, and it is no exaggeration to declare that his coordination theory has exerted an effect on inorganic chemistry comparable to that exerted on organic chemistry by the structural ideas of KEKULÉ, COUPER, LE BEL, and VAN'T HOFF.

In 1913, WERNER received the Nobel Prize in chemistry, the first Swiss chemist to attain this honor. Although he was chosen specifically for his monumental work on coordination compounds, the implications and applications of his research extend far beyond the confines of inorganic chemistry. Even before he began his extensive series of researches on "molecular compounds", he was vitally concerned with one of the most basic problems of chemistry — the nature of affinity and valence. Coordination compounds provided him with a challenging and exciting means to this end. The true nature and extent of his achievement is perhaps best expressed in the words of the Swedish Royal Academy of Sciences which awarded him the Nobel Prize in recognition of *"his work on the linkage of atoms in molecules,* by which he has thrown fresh light on old problems and opened new fields of research, particularly in inorganic chemistry" (italics added).

Today, when the practical and theoretical significance of modern structural inorganic chemistry is unquestioned, it is clear that the foundations of this field were erected largely by one man — ALFRED WERNER.

Chapter 1

Childhood and Youth

The genealogy of the WERNER family can be traced back as far as the sixteenth century. The family coat of arms *(Familienwappen)* (See cover) bears the date 1595. The oldest progenitor known with certainty is HANS WERNER DIT BÖTZ, a pastor at Eschbach/Baden, Germany, who died in Mulhouse (Haut-Rhin) in the province of Alsace in 1612. During succeeding years, members of the family resided in various places, but they never strayed far from the fertile and picturesque plain of the Rhine, which forms a natural boundary between France and Germany.

HANS-URBAN WERNER (born Mar. 8, 1784 in Siegen-Oberlauterbach [Bas-Rhin]), Alfred's paternal grandfather, was a farmer who later settled in Mulhouse, where he died on May 16, 1870. His marriage to CATHERINE GERHARDTSTEIN (1782—1854), also of Siegen, resulted in six sons and one daughter. One of these sons, JEAN-ADAM WERNER (born Sept. 18, 1820 in Siegen; died Mar. 26, 1893 in Mulhouse), Alfred's father, married BARBARA LÉGER of Oberseebach (Bas-Rhin), on Oct. 7, 1850. The childless marriage ended on June 14, 1854 with Barbara's death, and on Aug. 6, 1857, JEAN-ADAM WERNER remarried. His second wife, SALOMÉ JEANETTE TESCHÉ (born Jan. 9, 1825 in Molsheim (Bas-Rhin), France; died Mar. 1, 1903 in Mulhouse), was a daughter of FERDINAND TESCHÉ, originally from Remscheid, Germany and JEANETTE JETTER, originally from Freudenstadt, Germany. Of this union were born a daughter, Adèle (Sept. 26, 1858 — Oct. 2, 1858), and three sons, Adolf (Sept. 13, 1860 — Sept. 18, 1908), Jules (Feb. 16, 1862 — May 1, 1869), and Alfred. Only Adolf and Alfred lived to maturity.

ALFRED WERNER was born in Mulhouse at midnight on Dec. 12, 1866. During this same year, another Alfred — ALFRED NOBEL — invented dynamite and began to amass the huge fortune, which after his death was to be used for the prizes that mark the ultimate achievement in chemistry, physics, medicine, literature, and peace. Forty-seven years later, almost to the day, ALFRED WERNER was to receive the prize in chemistry.

Young WERNER was born at 1 rue Kléber, a building which still stands and whose ground floor is now occupied by a grocery store. The three-story house at the intersection of rue Kléber and rue du Manège is located not far from the foundry where Alfred's father, an iron worker, is said to have been employed.

The family must have moved soon, for most of WERNER's youth was spent in the large farmhouse at Altkirchenvorstadt 42 (now 21 faubourg d'Altkirch). The farm was a sprawling, active concern devoted mainly to dairying, and it encompassed many barns which housed cows, horses, and other domestic animals.

In Siegen, WERNER's father had been a locksmith. Later, in Mulhouse, as a foundry worker (*Eisendreher, torneur de fer),* he invented a number of farm implements, which were patented. Eventually, he apparently retired from formal employment and devoted himself to the family farm. One of his major hobbies was his rosegarden, which contained many rare and foreign species, and his son Alfred was later to develop a similar penchant for horticulture. The dominant figure in the WERNER household was the mother, a woman of acute intelligence and a member of the wealthy TESCHÉ family.

It is interesting to reflect for a moment on the immediate environment into which WERNER was born and to realize in how many ways it shaped and influenced his life and work.

Alsace has long cherished its independence, but of all the cities of this region, none valued its freedom more highly than did Mulhouse. As a result of the Treaties of Westphalia (1648) and the subsequent territorial usurpations of Louis XIV, by 1681 all of Alsace had become incorporated into France — with the sole exception of Mulhouse. Not until 1798 did this tiny republic, for economic reasons, voluntarily seek union with France. It was in this city of fiercely self-reliant and militantly autonomous citizens that ALFRED WERNER was born and raised. Eighteen sixty-six was the year of the Seven Weeks' War against Austria, which decided the hegemony of Prussia in Germany. Four years later the Franco-Prussian War began, bringing with it events that made a deep and lasting impression on young Alfred during his formative years.

When Alsace was annexed to the German Reich in 1871, more than 50,000 Alsatians, deeply French in spirit, chose to emigrate to France rather than remain under the dominion of the Germans. The WERNER family decided to remain in Mulhouse, but their sympathies remained entirely with France. Although by BISMARCK's unpopular decree German was the official language, French remained the language spoken in the WERNER home. The spirit of rebellion and resistance to authority, so much a part of WERNER's childhood, may well have contributed to the revolutionary and iconoclastic character of the theory with which his name is associated.

One of WERNER's earliest memories, dating from his fourth year, was that of shooting a toy gun at soldiers of the German army of occupation. A shell fragment from the siege of Strasbourg (Aug. 12 — Sept. 27, 1870) remained in his possession throughout his life; it eventually came to be used as a paperweight on his professorial desk in Zürich. During his student days at the *Polytechnikum* in Zürich, WERNER was to participate actively in "Stella", a student society whose goal was to further French language and culture, and one of the few non-technical elective courses which he then took was "The Franco-Prussian War". In short, despite his great reverence for German science, * WERNER's political and cultural ties bound him to France.

Like most of the WERNERS, Alfred's father was Catholic. His mother was originally Protestant but had been converted to Catholicism. Accordingly, at the age of six, young Alfred was enrolled at the *École Libre des Frères (Brüderschule)*, which he attended until his thirteenth year. This school, now under the direction of Père Simon, still operates at 18 porte du Miroir, and one can see the classrooms in which WERNER first learned to read and write as well as the small courtyard in which he played at recess.

During these early school years, the dominant traits of WERNER's personality — a remarkable self-confidence and a stubborn independence which made it impossible for him to submit blindly to authority — already became evident. He was not overly fond of school and often played truant. Whenever a paddling was imminent, he delighted in outwitting the brothers by hiding a piece of cardboard in his trousers. Yet his remarkable intellect was so obvious that once when he had to sit on the last row in a class seated according to scholastic achievement, his teacher said to him, "You could be first if you wanted to!"

It may be mentioned parenthetically that WERNER's early training in Catholicism had little effect on him; in later life, his interest in religion was minimal. He was

---

* The majority of WERNER's articles were to appear in German journals.

often to be seen working in the laboratory on Sundays, and in the *Universität Zürich* institute when he came upon *Assistenten* or *Dozenten* engaged in theological discussion, he would walk away with a scornful "Don't you have anything better to talk about?" His speculative mind and unquenchable curiosity, so obvious and predominant when applied to chemical matters, evidently found little of interest in the religious sphere.

Following his graduation from the *École des Frères* in 1878, WERNER entered the *École Professionelle (Höhere Gewerbeschule)*, a technical school. He attended this school, which is no longer in existence, until 1885. It was probably at about this time that WERNER's interest in chemistry took firm hold, and he began experimenting at home, with not always happy results. Tales of a bedroom ruined by a chemical explosion which almost caused Père WERNER to end a chemical career right then and there have drifted down to us. It may have been as an aftermath of this catastrophe that Alfred's experimental efforts were confined to the barn in the garden behind the house which became his first laboratory.

At the *École Professionelle*, WERNER became an outstanding student and won many prizes. Since school records are no longer available, it is not definitely known whether he studied chemistry at this time, but it appears extremely likely. A bright blue book containing 127 pages of elementary chemistry notes in his handwriting and bearing the title "Einleitung in die Chemie, Mulhouse 1883—84" dates from this period. That these notes were probably part of a formal chemistry course rather than a mere set of notes for home use is indicated by marginal notations and grades by a teacher. Here we see PCl_5 formulated as a "molecular compound" ($PCl_3 \cdot Cl_2$) in accordance with KEKULÉ's doctrine of constant valency. A decade later WERNER was to offer an alternative and much more satisfactory explanation for the constitution and configuration of "molecular compounds".

WERNER's preoccupation with classification, systematization, and isomeric relationships, probably a salient factor in his formulation of the coordination theory, is distinctly manifest in two holographs from this period. One of these contains page after page of structural formulas for organic isomers, arranged according to empirical formula. Another shows WERNER's habit of carefully collating and recording data in his small, neat script. This habit of note-taking, though later tempered with the moderation of maturity, continued unabated throughout his life. One needs only to compare these notes with others made a quarter-century later to see that the child was father to the man.

When we glance ahead into WERNER's later day-to-day notebooks, we find scientific data and personal notations intermingled with an utter disregard for the traditional dichotomy between professional and personal life. A daily record of his weight during a period of dieting is thus made with the same systematic thoroughness that characterized his scientific work. Even resolutions, which most of us usually make and break in a casual manner, were carefully committed to writing. "I won't buy myself any cigars until Christmas. — Alfred".

PAUL KARRER [1], PAUL PFEIFFER [2 (pp. 87—95), 3—6], and others have compared WERNER to AUGUST KEKULÉ (1829—1896) [7]. The comparison is an apt one, and we shall make use of it several times in this volume. WERNER, like KEKULÉ, was in his early years interested in architecture, and one is tempted to speculate whether architects and chemists require similar talents in dealing with the structural problems of their respective disciplines. In a book of WERNER's pencilled sketches made at the age of fifteen, we find that most of the drawings are of large and ornate buildings such as the famous Gothic cathedral at Rouen.

WERNER's earliest known original scientific work was written in Mulhouse at the age of eighteen, less than a month before he left for military service in the German army. "Without my own experimental data", he later recalled (*L 37* *), "I simply compiled a study of urea compounds which, in my youthful enthusiasm, I believed would reshape all of organic chemistry. . . . I went to the director of the *Chemieschule* in Mulhouse, Prof. [EMILIO] NOELTING [(1851—1922)] [8] . . . and showed him the work. He took it and told me to return in eight days. Punctually and in a hopeful mood I presented myself, but in spite of all the praise he accorded my work, he did not conceal from me the fact that I would not yet achieve a revolution in organic chemistry with this work and that I would have to study much more. I was satisfied to some extent with this [evaluation] and immediately asked him how long he thought I would need in order to become a professor. With a smile he answered that I would have to be patient for 7 or 8 years." Prof. NOELTING's prophecy was fulfilled eight years later when WERNER was called to *Universität Zürich* as successor to VIKTOR MERZ [2 (pp. 28—39)], (*A 82, A 132*).

The paper, entitled "Contribution de l'acide urique, de séries de la théobromine, caféine, et leurs derivés", poignantly, even touchingly, reveals the discrepancy between young WERNER's passionate, romantic enthusiasm for chemistry and his

---

* Numbers with letter prefixes refer to references listed in the specialized bibliographies at the end of the book.

still inadequate training in the subject. Although its style is banal and its chemical thinking often unsound, this work, in its broad scope and daring attempts at systematization, foreshadows the intellectual heights which WERNER was to reach only a few years later. One has only to compare this paper with WERNER's first published work, his inaugural dissertation "Über räumliche Anordnung der Atome in stickstoffhaltigen Molekülen" (*A 1, A 6*), to discern the tremendous strides, both in chemical knowledge and literary expression, which he made in four short years.

Today, largely as a result of EMIL FISCHER's [9] work in the late 1890's [10], the structure of purine and its derivatives has been experimentally established. A comparison of a few of WERNER's structures with FISCHER's structures will show that WERNER's proposals fell wide of the mark.

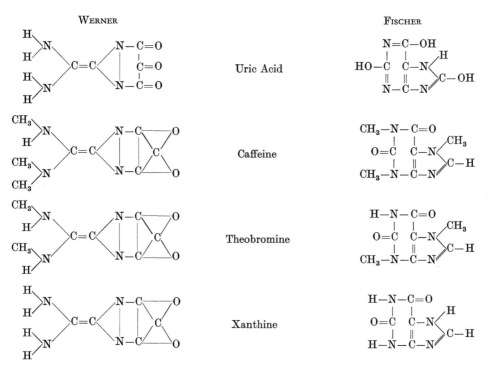

WERNER   FISCHER

Uric Acid

Caffeine

Theobromine

Xanthine

This youthful effort of WERNER's abounds with pompous exaggerations, and from NOELTING's marginal comments, of which "A little more modesty would be appropriate" is a typical example, we can almost visualize the older man cautiously attempting to encourage the young, impatient rebel and yet urging him to temper his enthusiasm with restraint and propriety. The manuscript, which clearly shows WERNER's awareness of, and unlimited faith in, his growing powers, ends with a jubilant burst of elation that borders on braggadocio. "This immense uric group has thus been developed with an extraordinary simplicity, and soon we shall have this area of organic chemistry arranged as orderly as few others are now arranged." WERNER's extravagantly rococo signature and the date, Sept. 15, 1885, end the paper with an almost theatrical flourish.

Two weeks after the completion of his urea paper, on Oct. 1, 1885, WERNER began his compulsory military duty in the German army as a one-year "volunteer" (Einjährig-Freiwilliger). Considering his antagonistic feelings toward Germany, the experience must have been a traumatic and ambivalent one. Yet it had its advantages. He was stationed in Karlsruhe, that charming and beautiful city in Baden noted for its public squares, ornate fountains, and stately monuments. The town had served as a model in the planning of Washington, D. C. In chemistry, of course, it is famed as the site of the first international chemical congress (1860), at which Cannizzaro explained the advantages of Avogadro's hypothesis in calculating atomic and molecular weights and thus put an end to the previous confusion in this fundamental area.

It was in this attractive and historic town that WERNER resided at Erbprinzen-strasse 32, a quarter-hour's walk from the *Grossherzogliches Schloss* (Grand Ducal Palace) where he often stood on sentry duty. He later recalled how, when Queen VICTORIA of Sweden * received him in Drottningholm Palace as the 1913 Nobel laureate in chemistry, he was able to tell her how he had been a sentry outside the palace where she had spent her childhood as a princess.

The recruit register (*Friedenstammrolle*) describes WERNER at this time as blond, slender (5 feet, 9 inches tall), and clean-shaven. The bushy mustache, so much a part of the mature WERNER, is not yet in evidence. On July 1, 1886, he became a lance corporal (*überzähliger Gefreiter*) and was considered suitable material for a non-commissioned officer.

About a man as renowned and with as forceful a personality as WERNER, many rumors accumulate in the course of time. A typical charge was that he settled in Switzerland because he had deserted from the German army and hence was never

---

* On Sept. 20, 1881, Princess VICTORIA of Baden married Crown Prince OSCAR GUSTAV ADOLF BERNADOTTE of Sweden, who later became King GUSTAV V.

allowed to set foot on German soil. His frequent trips and lectures in Germany show this rumor to be utterly without foundation, and his official military record confirms this fact.

While at Karlsruhe, WERNER availed himself of the opportunity to study chemistry at the *Grossherzogliche Technische Hochschule* (now the *Technische Hochschule Fridericiana),* where at this time the physicist HEINRICH HERTZ was in the process of discovering electromagnetic waves. On Oct. 13, 1885, WERNER enrolled as an auditor for the winter semester 1885/86 in two courses — "Chemistry of Carbon Compounds" (Prof. KELBE) and "Survey of Organic Chemistry" (Prof. KAST). As we shall see, it was only in 1892 shortly before his formulation of the coordination theory that he showed any deep interest in inorganic chemistry. His interest in *Geselligkeit,* however, is shown by his participation in "Gesellschaft Concordia", a student society dedicated to music, singing, and drinking.

Soon after leaving Karlsruhe, WERNER was to go to Zürich, Switzerland's largest city, where he was destined to spend the rest of his life. Yet Mulhouse remained close to WERNER's heart, and the city reciprocated by deciding on Sept. 6, 1965 to name a new street near the *École de Chimie* "rue Alfred Werner" in his honor. He paid Mulhouse frequent visits, especially before the death of his mother in 1903. He even planned but never completed a summer vacation home there. And every Christmas he would order from SCHEIDECKER FILS of Mulhouse what he evidently considered a very special *paté de fois gras in* "the same size my mother used to order".

Chapter 2

Student Years

Confirmed in his decision to study chemistry, WERNER lost no time in embarking on his academic career. On Oct. 1, 1886 he was officially discharged from the German army, and less than three weeks later, as a boarder with the SIMON ISRAEL family, he established his first residence in Zürich at Niederdorfstrasse 104, near the banks of the Limmat just down the hill from the *Eidgenössisches Polytechnikum,* where he enrolled for the winter semester 1886/87 in the *Chemisch-Technische Schule (Abteilung IV)* (Plate 3, page 66). He lived at the Niederdorfstrasse address from Oct. 19, 1886 to Dec. 1, 1888.

From the very first, WERNER was entranced by Zürich, one of the leading cultural, scientific, and artistic centers of Europe. But it was not only the intellectual atmosphere of the city appropriately called *Limmat-Athenes* which he found so congenial. The beautiful old city of Zwingli, fortunate in its location on the banks of the Limmat with the picturesque *Zürichsee* and the Alps in the distance, steeped in a history which radiated from the *Lindenhof,* once the site of an old Roman fort, and from the towering twin spires of the *Grossmünster* reputedly built by Charlemagne, must surely have impressed him as it has so many others. Within a remarkably short time, he felt completely at home in his adopted city, and he quickly became proficient in the local patois, *Züri-Dütsch,* perhaps understandably, for there are similarities between it and the Alsatian dialect of Mulhouse.

We can only speculate about WERNER's reasons for choosing the *Polytechnikum* in preference to Mulhouse's *École Supérieure de Chimie,* a venerable and reputable institution founded in 1822 which could boast of such names as PAUL SCHÜTZEN-BERGER, EMILIO NOELTING, and STANISLAUS VON KOSTANECKI on its faculty. Surely the youthful need to be on his own played its part in his decision. And, in addition, we may be fairly certain that he already realized that his abilities lay primarily in the theoretical realm and that the Mulhouse school, whose fame lay in the training of dye and textile chemists, would not provide him with a satisfying outlet for his natural talents. Very probably, Prof. NOELTING, to whom WERNER had shown his paper on urea, himself a graduate of the *Polytechnikum,* influenced WERNER in his choice of a school. However, a major factor must have been WERNER's political sentiments, for Alsace was at the time in a period of great tension. Anti-German feeling was running high. After the death on June 17, 1885 of the aged *Statthalter* (governor) of Alsace, Field Marshal VON MANTEUFFEL, who had pursued a policy of moderation, BISMARCK had launched a severe program of coercion against the population of Alsace. Strict police measures were resorted to in order to further the progress of Germanization, and many Alsatians, WERNER among them, were repelled and embittered by what they considered repressive restrictions on their freedom.

The *Eidgenössisches Polytechnikum* (since June 23, 1911 known as the *Eidgenössische Technische Hochschule* (Federal Institute of Technology or ETH) was then, as it is today, one of the foremost technical schools in the world [*11*]. Founded in 1855 and patterned after the famous *École Polytechnique* in Paris, by WERNER's time it had attracted to its faculty many outstanding luminaries, among whom, in the field of chemistry, may be mentioned VIKTOR MERZ (1839—1904; *Eidg. Poly.*, 1866—1870) (*A 82, A 132*), [*2* (pp. 28—39)], JOHANNES WISLICENUS (1835—1902; *Eidg. Poly.*, 1870—1872) [*2* (pp. 21—27), *12*], VICTOR MEYER (1848—1897; *Eidg. Poly.*, 1872—1885) [*13,14*], GEORG LUNGE (1839—1923; *Eidg. Poly.*, 1876—1907) [*15, 16*], HEINRICH GOLDSCHMIDT (1875—1937; *Eidg. Poly.*, 1881—1894) [*17*], FREDERIC P. TREADWELL (1857—1918; *Eidg. Poly.*, 1882—1918), and ARTHUR HANTZSCH (1857—1935; *Eidg. Poly.*, 1885—1893) [*18*]. Today the institution vies with the University of California in the number of Nobel Prize winners on its faculty.

As the graduate of a foreign, non-accredited industrial school, WERNER did not possess the Swiss *Maturitätsausweis* (maturity certificate), which permits a student to matriculate at any Swiss university without taking an entrance examination *(Aufnahme-Prüfung)*. The results of his examination are so revealing as to merit our detailed consideration. The grade in chemistry was, not unexpectedly, 6 (this being the highest and 1 the poorest grade), and the grades in most of the other subjects were satisfactory (drawing, 4, 5; natural sciences, $4^1/_2$; physics, $4^1/_2$; composition, 5; political and literary history, 6; and French, 6). The grades in mathematics, however, were 2 and $4^1/_2$. Even more surprising, in view of WERNER's amazing ability to conceive things structurally, are his failing grades ($1^1/_2$ and 2) in descriptive geometry. His deficiency in mathematics is confirmed by the grade of 2 which he received in "Higher Mathematics", a course taken during his first semester (winter, 1886/87). In view of his obvious weakness in this area, it is not surprising that throughout his entire career WERNER's contributions were essentially of a qualitative nature — even his celebrated conductivity studies with MIOLATI (*A 15, A 16, A 35*) are actually only semi-quantitative.

Today, coordination chemistry, like most branches of our science, is rapidly becoming more mathematical and abstract, a trend which will probably accelerate in the future. The power and advantages of such a mathematical approach are unquestionable. Yet we should never forget that the founder of coordination chemistry, a typical example of a non-quantitative genius, once failed mathematics in school. For those who are excessively preoccupied and enamored with the quantitative approach, WERNER should provide a dramatic proof that mathematical ability is not the only prerequisite for success in chemistry.

Closely allied to the growth in quantification, another of the trends which is partially responsible for the renaissance in inorganic chemistry since World War II is the increasing application of physical chemistry to the investigation of inorganic systems. If WERNER were alive today, he would undoubtedly possess strong opinions on this subject, for in a letter of June 23, 1904 to RICHARD LORENZ, editor of the *Zeitschrift für anorganische Chemie*, he resigned from the editorial board and announced his intention to found "a new inorganic journal which is primarily intended to become the organ of the purely chemical branch of inorganic chemistry". He cited the necessity for "a new organ of publication of this kind, inasmuch as the *Zeitschrift für anorganische Chemie* has gradually developed so strongly in the physicochemical direction that it no longer meets the needs and expectations of the pure inorganic chemist".* The proposed new journal, however, never materialized.

We should not construe this to mean that WERNER completely avoided the use of physicochemical methods in his work. Such a view is belied by his four classical studies in the *Zeitschrift für physikalische Chemie* (*A 15, A 16, A 35, A 66*) which are devoted to the conductivities of coordination compounds. In fact, he used conductivity measurements almost routinely in his elucidation of the constitution of complexes (*A 38, A 39, A 49, A 51, A 57, A 59, A 97*). He often resorted to cryoscopic (*A 39, A 49, A 51, A 57, A 66*) or ebullioscopic (*A 45, A 57*) determinations of molecular weights in order to obtain desired information about complexes and even used such determinations to calculate the VAN'T HOFF *i* factor (*A 39*) or the degree of hydration of salts (*A 66*). Furthermore, although he never published on the subject, several of the dissertations of his *Doktoranden* (doctoral candidates) [19] show him to have been one of the pioneers in the study of absorption spectra of inorganic complexes, a field later investigated in greater detail by several of his co-workers, of whom YUJI SHIBATA [20] is probably one of the most prominent. And if the measurement of optical rotation is considered to be a physico-

---

* The twentieth and final paper (*A 51*) (1899) in the series "Beitrag zur Konstitution anorganischer Verbindungen" was the last paper which WERNER published in the *Zeitschrift für anorganische Chemie*. From that time onward, the majority of his papers appeared in the *Berichte der Deutschen Chemischen Gesellschaft*.

chemical method, then WERNER's more than two dozen articles dealing with resolution and optical activity must be cited here. In short, WERNER never hesitated to apply physicochemical or quantitative methods to the solution of a problem which interested him, but he eschewed their use as an end in itself. He certainly would have disagreed vehemently with Lord KELVIN's cavalier denigration of non-quantitative science. *

But to return to WERNER's student days — we find that during his six semesters at the *Polytechnikum,* he naturally spent most of his time on courses in theoretical or applied chemistry. His teachers included ARTHUR HANTZSCH [18], GEORG LUNGE [15, 16], EMIL CONSTAM, FREDERIC P. TREADWELL, HEINRICH GOLDSCHMIDT [17], KARL HEUMANN (1850—1893), and JOHANNES BARBIERI. All his grades in these courses were at least 5 or above. In addition to the usual courses in physics, mineralogy, metallurgy, and other subjects required of a prospective chemist, WERNER also elected to take courses in Italian, the Franco-Prussian War, and Darwinism and Teleology.

In referring to these years, WERNER later recalled, "My teachers and fellow students learned to know me as a not always diligent, but always happy student" (*L 41*). Among his classmates who remained lifelong friends may be mentioned ARTURO MIOLATI (1869—1956) [23] (Plate 5, page 68), FRANZ FEIST, and ROLAND SCHOLL. In keeping with his gregarious nature, WERNER soon joined in the lighter side of student life. He became an active member of the student society "Stella" [24 (p. 796)], and he continued to participate in its affairs long after his graduation. This organization's purpose, above and beyond its purely social function, was to perpetuate French language and culture, a goal which corresponded closely with WERNER's own sympathies and interests.

In partial fulfillment of the requirements for his diploma, WERNER submitted a 48-page *Diplom-Arbeit* (undated, but written in 1888 or 1889), which is still

---

* "I often say that when you can measure what you are speaking about, and express it in numbers, you know something about it; but when you cannot express it in numbers, your knowledge is of a meagre and unsatisfactory kind; it may be the beginning of knowledge, but you have scarcely, in your thoughts, advanced to the stage of *Science,* whatever the matter may be."

The late nineteenth century was a time, of course, when faith in science, especially quantitative science, knew no bounds. Even SVANTE ARRHENIUS (1859—1927) [21] insisted upon a distinction between hypothesis, which he regarded as nonquantitative, and theory, which he considered quantitative [22].

preserved in bound but holograph form. The work, which was supervised by Profs. GEORG LUNGE and ARTHUR HANTZSCH, consists of five preparations, both inorganic and organic: (1) "Carbon Disulfide from 300 g. of Sulfur," (2) "Sodium Nitroprusside from 500 g. of Potassium Ferrocyanide," (3) "Phenylhydrazine from 300 g. of Aniline," (4a) "Fluorescein from 500 g. of Benzene," and (4b) "Reaction of Fluorescein with Aqueous Ammonia in a Bomb." The apparatus for the preparation of carbon disulfide (see plate on p. 15) is typical of the four carefully drawn illustrations which are included in the work. The various sections of the report received grades ranging from $4^3/_4$ to 6. After passing his oral and practical examinations (Oct., 1888; July, 1889), WERNER reached his first academic goal. On Aug. 3, 1889 he was awarded the degree of *Technischer Chemiker*.

WERNER now became an unsalaried assistant *(Hilfsassistent)* in GEORG LUNGE's chemical-technical laboratory (1889—1890). According to one source, ERNST BERL [25], LUNGE was responsible for WERNER's advanced studies under MARCELLIN * BERTHELOT (1827—1907) [26] in 1891. The story goes that after WERNER had spent one semester as an assistant, LUNGE fired him because "you are much too good for this minor position". LUNGE then added, "I know that your father is a man of little means. With his and my help it may be possible for you to study a year in Paris" [16]. BERL further states (B 4) that LUNGE later completely financed WERNER's postdoctoral semester with BERTHELOT.

We know that WERNER's father was not in favor of his son's study of chemistry but had other hopes for him.** We also know that both NOELTING and LUNGE encouraged the elder WERNER to allow Alfred to continue his education. However, WERNER himself and others who were close to him have never mentioned or confirmed the story of LUNGE's financial assistance, and certain discrepancies in its details lead this author to doubt its authenticity.

While still *Hilfsassistent* to LUNGE, WERNER began work on his doctoral dissertation under HANTZSCH's direction. Only nine years WERNER's senior, HANTZSCH, at the age of twenty-eight, had been called in 1885 as full *(ordinarius)* professor to succeed VICTOR MEYER at the *Polytechnikum*. His reputation had been securely established by his well-known pyridine synthesis (1882). One of the characteristics

---

* The incorrect spelling "MARCELIN" is often found in the literature.

** "Perhaps I would have done better to go into a factory," WERNER wrote his parents on June 21, 1890, "but I confess that I believe a scientific career is my vocation; and I have been told this so often that I am finally forced to believe it."

14

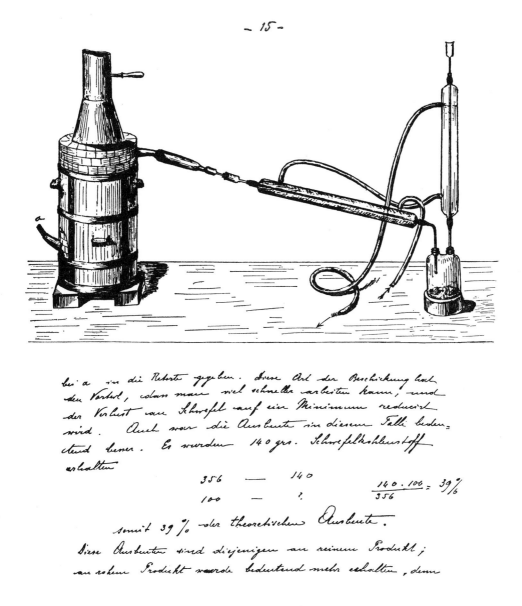

bei a in die Retorte gegeben. Diese Art der Beschickung hat
den Vorteil, dass man viel schneller arbeiten kann, und
der Verlust an Schwefel auf ein Minimum reducirt
wird. Auch war die Ausbeute in diesem Falle bedeutend besser. Es wurden 140 grs. Schwefelkohlenstoff
erhalten

$$356 \quad — \quad 140$$
$$100 \quad — \quad ? \qquad \frac{140 \cdot 100}{356} = 39\%$$

somit 39 % der theoretischen Ausbeute.

Diese Ausbeuten sind diejenigen an reinem Produkt;
an rohem Produkt wurde bedeutend mehr erhalten, denn

Diplom-Arbeit, Eidgenössisches Polytechnikum (ca. 1888), Page 15, showing apparatus for the preparation of carbon disulfide

of his research was the use of a variety of widely differing methods in order to obtain the desired information about a given chemical system, a *modus operandi* which WERNER was also to follow. Despite HANTZSCH's more than five hundred publications, his greatest discovery was probably ALFRED WERNER, who was not only his most outstanding pupil but also his lifelong friend.

In many ways, the two men offer a strange study in contrasts (Plate 8, page 70). HANTZSCH was slender, reserved, abstemious, and controlled, whereas WERNER inclined toward corpulence, was hearty and robustly humorous in company, well-known for his enjoyment of alcohol and tobacco, and at times impulsive — even temperamental. According to WERNER's student, colleague, and "chief of staff" at the Chemical Institute of *Universität Zürich*, PAUL PFEIFFER (1875—1951), who was also acquainted with HANTZSCH, WERNER clearly surpassed his teacher in originality and creative talent *(Genialität)*, a fact which HANTZSCH readily admitted [6 (p. 23)].

HANTZSCH was not only an intense and inspiring lecturer but also a remarkable research director. His laboratory was characterized by a vibrant scientific atmosphere, in which *Doktoranden* were encouraged to think independently and to trust their own judgment. In his twice-daily, lively discussions with his *Doktoranden,* into which he brought his disciplined, knowledgeable, and highly demanding standards, new views were respected, and controversy was encouraged. Even after HANTZSCH left Zürich for Würzburg in 1893, he and WERNER maintained an extensive correspondence and usually managed to find the opportunity to meet several times a year. WERNER always regarded HANTZSCH as the outstanding influence in his early career, and he dedicated his first text, "Lehrbuch der Stereochemie" (*T 1*),* to his former teacher, "who, with mature judgment, knew how to guide [my initial scientific efforts] in the right direction" (letter to HANTZSCH, Apr. 13, 1904).

It was in the span of three short but eventful years (1890—1893) that WERNER produced his three most important theoretical papers — "three giant steps" *(drei gewaltige Schritte),* as his former student and assistant ROBERT HUBER has so aptly

---

* HANTZSCH himself wrote a short text "Grundriss der Stereochemie" (Eduard Trewendt, Breslau, 1893), to which WERNER contributed a section on inorganic complexes. The book was translated into French ("Précis de Stéréochimie," Georges Carré, Paris, 1896), which in turn was translated into English ("The Elements of Stereochemistry," Chemical Publishing Co., Easton, Pa., 1901).

called them (*B 12*). The first of this illustrious trio was the inaugural dissertation (1890) (*A 6*), which actually consists of four parts, three of which were published separately — (1) "Über räumliche Anordnung der Atome in stickstoffhaltigen Molekülen" (*A 1*), (2) "Über ein zweites Benzoïnoxim" (*A 3*), (3) "Versuch zur Darstellung stereochemisch isomerer Körper der Furfuraldoximreihe" (*A 4*), and (4) "Über die angeblich isomeren Paraamidoazobenzolsulfonsäuren" (unpublished).

The first or theoretical part, which appeared under the joint authorship of HANTZSCH and WERNER even before the dissertation itself was printed, was not only WERNER's first publication, but it still remains his most popular and important work in the organic field. In this paper, which has been translated into English (*A 1 [a]*), WERNER and HANTZSCH, by transferring the LE BEL [27] and VAN'T HOFF [28] concept of the tetrahedral carbon atom (1874) to the nitrogen atom, were able to explain a great number of puzzling cases of geometric isomerism. For the first time, the stereochemistry of nitrogen compounds was placed on a firm and satisfactory theoretical basis.

ERNST BERL (*B 4*) recounts how WERNER suggested to HANTZSCH that the three valences of the nitrogen atom are oriented toward the three corners of a tetrahedron, the fourth corner of which is occupied by the nitrogen atom itself (see plate on p. 18). According to BERL, HANTZSCH at first did not accept this viewpoint, but on the following day he told WERNER that he believed his idea to be correct. HANTZSCH (*A 1*) was careful to acknowledge WERNER's major role in the development of the new concept, which he described as "essentially the intellectual property of Herr WERNER". According to HANTZSCH, WERNER was the only one who "clearly grasped the basic idea with its most important consequences when others only vaguely expressed the thought that perhaps nitrogen could also give rise to geometric isomerism, in a manner similar to carbon".

In all fairness to HANTZSCH, however, it must be admitted that despite a number of publications on oximes and other organic nitrogen derivatives by WERNER, it was primarily HANTZSCH's numerous subsequent researches, particularly on aromatic azo and diazo compounds, that won acceptance for the new theory. Although he continued to publish occasionally on organic topics throughout his scientific career, WERNER's attention soon shifted to inorganic chemistry.

In spite of early attacks on the theory by VICTOR MEYER [13, 14] and KARL VON AUWERS (1863—1939) [29] and later attacks by EUGEN BAMBERGER (1857—1932)

dass nach v. Baye's Spannungstheorie bei Eintritt mehrfacher Bindung und nach J. Wislicenus durch die gegenseitige Einwirkung der an das Kohlenstoffatom gebundenen Gruppen die Valenzen dieses Atoms aus ihrer ursprünglichen Richtung abgelenkt werden, so ist es doch gerade im Sinne der räumlichen Vorstellungen von Wislicenus ganz undenkbar, dass für Verbindungen, wie $HC \equiv N$, $(C_6H_5) \equiv N$ u. s. w. die drei an Stickstoff gebundenen Kohlenstoffvalenzen in eine Ebene fallen sollten. Daraus folgt aber nothwendig, dass für Verbindungen vom Typus $XC \equiv N$ die drei Valenzen des Stickstoffatoms ebenfalls nicht in eine Ebene fallen können. Muss diese Thatsache aber in diesen speziellen Fällen zugegeben werden, so ist nicht mehr einzusehen, warum unter andern Bedingungen die Valenzen des dreiwerthigen Stickstoffs nicht auch in anderer Weise zur Wirkung kommen könnten als in einer Ebene, und diese Schlussfolgerung ergiebt die Grundhypothese der folgenden Entwicklungen:

Die drei Valenzen des Stickstoffatoms kommen bei gewissen Verbindungen in den Ecken eines (jedenfalls nicht regulären) Tetraeders zur Wirkung in dessen vierter Ecke sich das Stickstoffatom selbst befindet.

Dissertation, "Über räumliche Anordnung der Atome in stickstoffhaltigen Molekülen", *Universität Zürich*, 1890, Page 23

18

[30] and other chemists extending several decades into the present century [31], WERNER and HANTZSCH's view has withstood the test of time, and today, with only slight modification, it takes its rightful place alongside the LE BEL and VAN'T HOFF concept of the tetrahedral carbon atom as one of the cornerstones of stereochemistry.

In July of 1890, WERNER's dissertation was "approved very favorably" *(sehr günstig begutachtet)* by Profs. HARUTHIUN ABELJANZ (1849—1921) [2 (pp. 47—48), 32] and VIKTOR MERZ [2 (pp. 28—39)], *(A 82, A 132)* of the *Zürcher Hochschule* (which in the summer session of 1912 became officially known as *Universität Zürich,* by which name it shall be referred to in this volume).* These gentlemen found his written examination to be "quite outstanding" *(ganz ausgezeichnet).* ABELJANZ later described the dissertation as "an outstanding achievement, which has not only contributed materially to the explanation of well-known cases of geometric isomerism but has also led to numerous discoveries of new stereoisomeric compounds". In keeping with his organic interests at this time, WERNER's *Clausurarbeit* (final paper) dealt with the topic "Über die Theorie der aromatischen Verbindungen". In the words of Prof. ABELJANZ, it "showed that [WERNER] possesses extensive literary knowledge and thinks quite independently". The cumulative effect of all these achievements was that on Oct. 13, 1890 the twenty-three-year-old ALFRED WERNER was awarded the degree *Doktor der Philosophie "unter besonderer Anerkennung vorzüglicher Leistung"* (with special recognition of superior performance). He had made the most of the guidance of his mentors. Now he was ready to strike out completely on his own.

Chapter 3

Early Successes

"I already sense around me a certain cordiality of manner which everyone is anxious to let me feel," WERNER wrote to his parents on May 11, 1891. It was his dissertation which had earned him not only the doctorate but also that "certain

---

* The *Polytechnikum* was not empowered to grant the doctoral degree until 1909. Hence, although WERNER's work was done under HANTZSCH's direction at the *Polytechnikum,* the degree was formally awarded by the *Universität.*

cordiality" from the scientific world. But WERNER was not content to rest upon his laurels. "I am beginning to take my place among the chemists of the time, and if heaven preserves my health, I intend to surpass them one by one, for glory is not an empty word; it is the personal satisfaction of a man who needs it as a stimulant in his moments of weakness."

In later life, WERNER was extremely reticent about his emotions, aspirations, and feelings. This letter, then, is almost unique in giving a rare glimpse into the feelings of the young WERNER, his *Weltanschauung*, his growing sense of self-identity, and his joyous, passionate, and almost religious devotion to chemistry. "My illusions have never left me, but man needs them, for without illusions there is no ideal. I am becoming an enthusiast with age; * I often remain for long moments in ecstasy before the beauties of my science, for the more I advance into its mysteries, the more it seems to me grand, sublime, almost too beautiful for a mere mortal."

Although WERNER, with his superb self-confidence, seems to have accepted the financial assistance of his parents as a right rather than a privilege, he was still ambivalent about his pecuniary dependence upon them. "I often ask myself when the moment will arrive when I can earn my own living," he wrote them on Mar. 18, 1891. "Seeing that this date is still distant, I almost regret having chosen an academic career. Then I again resume my work with even greater vigor, but this only makes me a scholar; it gives me some fame but until now not a *sou* ** . . . How often I have cherished the idea that once I have become a *Privat-Dozent*, *** my brother and I could buy a small factory in the vicinity [of Mulhouse], which I would manage while he would take care of the commercial part. **** Again, it is one of those beautiful illusions which disappear at the moment when one believes it to be closest."

But a *Privat-Dozentur* required the *venia legendi* or *venia docendi*, the privilege of lecturing at a university, which was awarded only upon acceptance by the

---

* WERNER was all of twenty-four at the time!

** This letter, like all of WERNER's correspondence with his parents, is in French.

*** An unsalaried university lecturer whose sole income is derived from *Kollegiengelder* — fees paid by the students who enroll in his courses (at that time *ca.* Sw. Fr. 5 per student per semester-hour).

**** This sentence is apparently intended to placate WERNER's parents. There is no evidence that he ever seriously considered any career but chemistry, which, as we shall see, was for him not only a full-time job, but almost a way of life. His brother Adolf later acquired a pig-breeding farm at Tiefengraben in Mulhouse.

faculty of a *Habilitationsschrift,* a paper embodying the results of original and independent research. With his characteristic single-minded determination, WERNER set about compiling such a paper. During the busy years 1890 and 1891, he had been conducting his own research on benzhydroxamic acid derivatives in the analytical laboratories of the *Polytechnikum,* and these results served as the experimental and subordinate part of his *Habilitationsschrift* (Oct., 1891) (*A 8*), "Über Stereochemie des Stickstoffs in der Benzhydroxamsäurereihe" (*A 10, A 11*).

In his evaluation (*Gutachten*, Dec. 5, 1891) of this section of the *Habilitationsschrift*, HANTZSCH declared that "Herr WERNER has succeeded in the task, previously attempted without success by a number of well-known investigators, of solving the problem of the quite complicated isomeric relationships between certain hydroxylamine derivatives, at least in principle". He admitted that some of the descriptive passages were "often rather awkward and obscure and therefore probably not easy to understand for those not familiar with the subject". He also added that the "punctuation and style are also frequently careless or at least seem so; for example, the subjects in main and secondary clauses change almost regularly; the experiments are too often simply written down one after another and are not related to one another by brief notes explaining their significance. Such faults are, however, subordinate to the total achievement; moreover, in my experience, they appear almost regularly in first publications and are perhaps even more excusable in the case of Herr Dr. WERNER, an Alsatian."

In the first and theoretical part of his *Habilitationsschrift,* "Beiträge zur Theorie der Affinität und Valenz," the fledgling doctor of philosophy chose to attack no less than the supreme patriarch of structural organic chemistry, AUGUST KEKULÉ [7] himself. In this, his second "giant step" in stereochemistry, WERNER attempted to replace KEKULÉ's concept of rigid directed valencies with his own more flexible approach, in which he viewed affinity as a variously divisible, attractive force emanating from the center of an atom and acting equally in all directions (See plate on p. 22). By the use of this new concept and without assuming directed valencies, WERNER was able to derive the VAN'T HOFF configurational formulas. Although this paper contains the seeds which later were to flower forth in the primary valence *(Hauptvalenz)* and secondary valence *(Nebenvalenz)* of the co-ordination theory, it deals exclusively with organic compounds.

WERNER was aware of the serious nature of his attack upon the current, firmly entrenched valence theory, and he fully expected strong resistance to his new ideas.

Raum ist einheitlicher Materie und der Einfachheit halber kugelförmig gedacht wird, so werde bezüglich der Affinität folgende einfache Annahme gemacht und als Basis für sämmtliche weitere Entwickelungen betrachtet: *Die Affinität ist eine, vom Centrum des Atoms gleichmäßig nach allen Seiten seiner Kugeloberfläche wirkende, anziehende Kraft.*

Aus dieser Auffassung der Affinität folgt nothwendig, dass gesonderte Valenzeinheiten nicht bestehen. Die Valenz bedeutet ein von Valenzeinheiten unabhängiges, empirisch gefundenes Zahlenverhältniss, in welchem die Atome sich miteinander verbinden. Sie ist nicht

Dem Einwurf, dass durch die Annahme von Valenzeinheiten die Zahlenverhältnisse, in welchen die Atome sich miteinander verbinden erklärt werden, muss entgegengehalten werden, dass eine derartige Vorstellung keine Erklärung, sondern nur eine Umschreibung dieser Erscheinung bedeutet.

Habilitationsschrift, "Beiträge zur Theorie der Affinität und Valenz", *Eidgenössisches Polytechnikum*, 1891, Page 9

In a letter of Apr. 4, 1891 to his parents, he seems eager to test his strength in the coming struggle. "A second theoretical work [the *Habilitationsschrift*], more daring than the first [the dissertation], is in press in Germany.* As it will appear under my name alone, I shall have to defend myself singlehandedly against all attacks; I hope to emerge victorious, but the battle will be heated."

But WERNER's anticipated battle did not take place, at least at that time. Even before the entire *Habilitationsschrift* was printed, this important paper was published separately in a journal of limited circulation, the *Vierteljahrsschrift der Zürcher Naturforschenden Gesellschaft* (*A 7*), where it elicited little notice until brought to the attention of the scientific world by a discussion of its concepts in WERNER's "Lehrbuch der Stereochemie" (1904) (*T 1*).

In his *Gutachten*, HANTZSCH described this portion of the *Habilitationsschrift* as "an achievement which stands far above the ordinary and [which] represents a significant advance in the field of theoretical chemistry, although for the present it consists mainly of the elimination of incorrect and damaging views on valence and the so-called valence units *(Valenzeinheiten)*". "With this paper, the author has proven himself to possess extraordinary originality, [and he] has also very fortunately overcome the difficulty in presenting his ideas clearly and comprehensibly." In conclusion, regarding both sections of the work, HANTZSCH remarked that "on the whole, ... the *Habilitationsschrift* of Herr Dr. WERNER may be judged as not only a good, but an excellent scientific achievement. Just as the earlier ... works of the same author, in spite of their small number, have already made his name well known, so his *Habilitationsschrift* will be noted and appreciated in wider chemical circles."

"While I shall not habilitate myself until the beginning of the [winter 1891/92] semester," WERNER wrote his parents on May 11, 1891, "HANTZSCH has told me that nevertheless I could already begin lecturing before next semester [winter 1891/92] but that he does not advise me to do so. Instead, he advises me to go abroad during this semester, as is the custom, and to begin my teaching with the summer [1892] semester." WERNER had intended to go to England, but HANTZSCH advised him that "the best place that I could choose would be Paris, the Sorbonne,

---

* Since the paper appeared in a Swiss journal, this statement, together with WERNER's remarks to HANTZSCH in a letter of July 2, 1902, may indicate that the *Habilitationsschrift* was originally sent to a German journal, most probably *Berichte*, but was rejected.

since the old French chemistry, with its fine methods, is still practiced there".*
In attempting to justify the expenses of his intended trip, WERNER remarked that
"Zürich is not large enough for one who must later teach science to young people.
It is absolutely necessary that I go abroad for one semester in order to enlarge my
scientific horizons and to get some idea of how our science is practiced elsewhere.
For this, a stimulating *milieu* is necessary, where all the human sciences are united,
and for this, Paris is surely the best place." **

On Oct. 16, 1891, from the Hotel *Pfauen* where he now resided, WERNER submitted
his recently completed *Habilitationsschrift* to the *Hohe Schweizerische Schulrat*
and petitioned them for the *venia docendi* in chemistry at the *Polytechnikum*. He
did not sit back and wait or worry about its acceptance but almost immediately
departed for Paris in order to pursue research in thermochemistry under the
direction of the illustrious French physical chemist, historian of chemistry, and
statesman, MARCELLIN BERTHELOT (1827—1907) [26].

Although some sources report that WERNER spent an entire year at the *Collège
de France*, WERNER himself says that he worked there only during the winter
semester 1891/92. Virtually nothing is known of his sojourn in Paris, save the fact
that he frequented the *Brasserie Balzar* in the vicinity of the *Collège*. Unfortunately, the records of foreigners residing in Paris which is now kept on file at the
Préfecture de Police was begun only in 1923, and the *Collège de France* has never
kept matriculation records. The director has always had the privilege of permitting
anyone to work in his laboratory whom he judges as capable, without any
administrative formality — a liberal and commendable policy but one not
conducive to historiography.

"With BERTHELOT in Paris I learned that one could also solve chemical problems
with concepts other than those customary in chemistry at that time," WERNER
later remarked (*L 37*). A perusal of his lecture notes, which show a definite
emphasis on thermochemical data, confirms his statement. Nevertheless, the most
quantitative use that he ever made of thermodynamic data was the addition and
subtraction of energy changes accompanying chemical reactions.

---

* CHARLES-ADOLPHE WURTZ, it will be recalled, in obvious reference to LAVOISIER, once made
the controversial and chauvinistic statement: *"La chimie, c'est une science française."*
** The author cannot resist the temptation of quoting here LIEBIG's cynical advice to the young
KEKULÉ, who like WERNER went to Paris during his early twenties to complete his chemical
education. *"Gehen Sie nach Paris, da erweitern Sie Ihren Gesichtskreis, da lernen Sie eine neue
Sprache, da lernen Sie das Leben einer Großstadt kennen, aber Chemie lernen Sie dort nicht."*

Two published works stem from WERNER's Paris period. "Sur un nitrate basique de calcium" (*A 9*), an admittedly minor work, details the preparation and measurement of the heat of formation of the compound $Ca(NO_3)_2 \cdot Ca(OH)_2 \cdot 2^{1}/_{2}\text{-}3\,H_2O$ and has the distinction of being WERNER's "Opus 1" in the inorganic field. A lecture, "La stéréochimie de l'azote," which was delivered in Paris in 1892 and later appeared in a book (*L 1*), elaborated upon the topic of his doctoral dissertation.

On Jan. 4, 1892, while WERNER was still at work in Paris with BERTHELOT, the *Hohe Schweizerische Schulrat,* which had accepted his *Habilitationsschrift,* named him *Privat-Dozent* in the *Freifächerabtheilung* (elective subjects division) of the *Polytechnikum.* For the subject of the public inaugural address *(Antrittsvorlesung)* required of every new *Privat-Dozent* sometime during his first year of teaching, WERNER chose the perenially popular "benzene problem", which he had already touched upon in his *Habilitationsschrift.* In this lecture, "Kritische Beleuchtung der heutigen Benzoltheorie", * which was delivered during the summer semester 1892, he first reviewed and called attention to the inadequacies of the various structural formulas proposed for benzene by KEKULÉ, CLAUS, LOSCHMIDT, THOMSEN, SACHSE, and other chemists. He then presented his own views, which had already been developed in the *Habilitationsschrift.* By assuming that affinity is a force transmitted by a process akin to the emission of light, he showed how some of the atoms in the benzene ring would be brightly illuminated while others would be placed in the shade. This clever analogy permitted him to explain many experimentally observed aspects of aromatic substitution — again without invoking directed valence forces.

WERNER's first course, "Atomic Theory" (1 hour), was given at the *Polytechnikum* during the summer semester 1892 (Apr. 19 — Aug. 6). In the early years of his teaching career, he was handicapped by factors often common to novice instructors — youth and inexperience. In addition to intellectual gifts, it took extreme tact, a character trait for which WERNER was never noted, to build and preserve good relations with both students and colleagues. At this time, he grew a mustache

---

* This lecture is available in holograph form only, but its main conclusions have been published elsewhere, *e. g.,* on pp. 370—377 of WERNER's "Lehrbuch der Stereochemie" (*T 1*) or on pp. 10—13, 27, and 82—86 of a small, obscure, and now rare book by ERNST BLOCH on WERNER's theory of the carbon atom and the stereochemistry of carbocyclic compounds (*B 5*). The topic of WERNER's *Probevorlesung* (trial lecture delivered to the faculty by a prospective *Dozent* before the *venia legendi* is granted) is not known, but it was most probably organic.

and beard (Plates 4, page 67, and 5, page 68) so as to appear older and more authoritative to his students, who were only a few years younger than he. The beard soon disappeared, but the inseparable mustache remained with him throughout his lifetime.

During the winter semester 1892/93 (Oct. 10, 1892 — Mar. 18, 1893), WERNER taught "Selected Topics in Inorganic Chemistry" and "Comparative Organic Chemistry", both one-hour courses. The last course that he taught at the *Polytechnikum* was "Stereochemistry", a twice-weekly lecture, largely on organic compounds, presented during the summer semester 1893 (Apr. 11 — Aug. 3). For the winter semester 1893/94 (Oct. 9, 1893 — Mar. 17, 1894), he was scheduled to repeat his inorganic lecture and also to teach a one-hour course on "The Chemistry of Naphthalene, Anthracene, and Higher Nuclei", but these courses were never given, for on Sept. 29, 1893 WERNER left the *Polytechnikum* to accept a call to *Universität Zürich*.

The university [33] had been founded in 1833, and until the *Polytechnikum* was founded in 1855, it was the sole source of chemical research in Zürich. For many years, it was customary for *Professoren* and *Dozenten* to teach simultaneously at both institutions, but by the time that WERNER had joined the university, these "double professorships" *(Doppelprofessuren* or *Parallelprofessuren)* had ceased.

The experimental activity of the first occupant of the chair of chemistry at the university, KARL JAKOB LÖWIG (1803—1890; Univ. Zh., 1833—1853) [2 (pp. 11—13)], was extremely limited during his first decade at Zürich, for the laboratory, which served both the *Universität* and *Kantonsschule,* was merely an improvised affair located in the building of the *Carolinum "in der Chorherren"*, on the Kirchgasse near the *Grossmünster* [2 (p. 3 ff.)]. The situation improved somewhat with the erection in 1842 of a laboratory in the new *Kantonsschule*. In 1861, during the tenure of LÖWIG's successor, GEORG ANDREAS KARL STÄDELER (1821—1871; Univ. Zh., 1853—1870) [2 (pp. 17—20)], a new laboratory, shared with the *Polytechnikum* until 1887, was erected on the Rämistrasse, and it was in this building that WERNER was to perform the major portion of his life's work. We shall later (Chap. 8) have occasion to examine in detail its inadequacies and WERNER's consequent frustrations in carrying out research within its narrow confines.

Although the cantonal university's chemistry faculty was not graced with quite the array of illustrious figures as was the federal *Polytechnikum's* faculty, it nevertheless had its share of prominent chemists. By the time of WERNER's call

(1893), its staff had included MATTHIAS EDUARD SCHWEIZER (1818—1860; Univ. Zh., 1841—1860) [2 (pp. 14—16)] of SCHWEIZER's reagent fame, JOHANNES WISLICENUS (1835—1902; Univ. Zh., 1860—1872) [2 (pp. 21—27), 12] and the joint team of VIKTOR MERZ (1839—1904; Univ. Zh., 1866—1893) [2 (pp. 28—39)], (A 82, A 132) and WILHELM WEITH (1846—1881; Univ. Zh., 1866—1881) [2 (pp. 40—46)]. As far back as 1872, the Chemisches Institut had become large enough to be subdivided into two divisions — Laboratorium A for the training of chemists under the direction of MERZ and Laboratorium B for the training of medical and education students (Mediziner und Lehramtskandidaten) under the direction of HARUTHIUN ABELJANZ (1849—1921; Univ. Zh., 1873—1920) [2 (pp. 47—48), 32]. As MERZ's successor, WERNER was entrusted with the direction of Laboratorium A. This assignment of duties was later to lead to a conflict with ABELJANZ as we shall see.

The call to Universität Zürich came about largely because of the almost overnight fame which WERNER had received as a result of the publication of his most important theoretical paper, his third and greatest "giant step", "Beitrag zur Konstitution anorganischer Verbindungen" (A 14), in which he had proposed the basic postulates of his epoch-making coordination theory. Unlike his Habilitationsschrift, this paper did not appear in an obscure journal but in the third volume (1893) of the recently founded (1892) Zeitschrift für anorganische Chemie, where it aroused instantaneous interest — and criticism.

We shall now depart momentarily from our strictly chronological narrative in order to examine the circumstances of WERNER's call to the university. Then, with the young Ausserordentlicher Professor firmly entrenched in his new position, we shall consider his coordination theory, which logically leads to a birdseye view of his life's work.

In June of 1893, a four-man faculty commission (Profs. ALFRED KLEINER [1849—1916], physics [president]; HARUTHIUN ABELJANZ, chemistry; ALBERT HEIM [1847—1937], geology; and ARNOLD LANG [1855—1914], zoology) was appointed to select a successor to VIKTOR MERZ, who, for reasons of health and age, was retiring from the chair of chemistry at the university. The commission seriously considered three candidates after eliminating ten others on the basis of opinions received from a number of prominent chemists, including ADOLF VON BAEYER, JOHANNES WISLICENUS, EMIL FISCHER, VICTOR MEYER, ARTHUR HANTZSCH, and ROBERT GNEHM. Of these three — Ausserordentlicher Prof. HANS

VON PECHMANN (1850—1904) [34] of Munich, *Ausserordentlicher Prof. F. K. JOHANNES THIELE* (1865—1927) [35] also of Munich, and *Privat-Dozent* ALFRED WERNER of Zürich — the last named was the youngest and least known, partly because his most significant achievement, the coordination theory, had been published only a few months earlier.

Yet those who did know WERNER and his work, especially HANTZSCH, FISCHER, and VON BAEYER, were so impressed by his "extraordinary gifts, especially in theoretical work" that they ranked him above THIELE as the equal of VON PECH-MANN, thirteen years his senior. HANTZSCH described the coordination theory as "the most significant [work] that has appeared in years in the field of pure chemistry; truly revolutionary" *(geradezu bahnbrechend)*, while FISCHER remarked that "this work bears witness to an extraordinary talent for treating a whole series of apparently divergent facts from new unified viewpoints".

The commission's only reservation was that WERNER might not have had enough practical experience to be able to administer a laboratory. These doubts, however, were dispelled by HANTSZCH, who expressed great confidence in his pupil in this regard. BERTHELOT, with whom WERNER had worked the previous year, concurred with this evaluation. Professors KLEINER and HEIM were then delegated to attend WERNER's lectures at the *Polytechnikum*. Their impressions were highly favorable; they praised his "sovereign mastery of his subject" and found him "clear and fluent in delivery" and "not without warmth and spirit".

Still, for a time, arguments were presented on behalf of each of the candidates, and the excitement and suspense grew. According to PAUL KARRER, WERNER felt the need to withdraw physically from the fray, and so he retreated to the Zermatt mountains where he awaited the outcome of the deliberations. At any rate, we are certain that on June 26, 1893 he was in Zürich, for it was on this Monday evening at the *Zunfthaus zur Zimmerleuten* that all the commission members had an opportunity to hear him address the *Zürcher Naturforschende Gesellschaft* on the topic "Über die Konstitution anorganischer chemischer Verbindungen" (*L 3*). This lecture convinced them that WERNER possessed extraordinary ability, both as a scientist and as a lecturer. "All expressed the wish to obtain *that* man and to win him for the university."

Parenthetically, the commission admitted also being influenced by the fact that WERNER had given up his German citizenship and was in the process of becoming a Swiss citizen. Surely this would be assurance that he would be more likely than the other candidates to stay at the university for "a longer period" — a prophetic wish!

Prophetic too, of struggles to come, was the commission's remark that the other candidates, being older and already established professionally, might not be eager to work at a not overgenerous salary in "laboratory facilities which are neither large nor otherwise very inviting". We shall soon see how WERNER coped with these facilities, so aptly named "Catacombs".

Two final requirements demanded of new prospective faculty members, the *Habilitationsschrift* and the *Probevorlesung* were fulfilled by WERNER with remarkable ease. He early requested (June 7, 1893) that his "Beitrag zur Konstitution anorganischer Verbindungen" *(A 14)* be accepted as his *Habilitationsschrift*. Prof. ABELJANZ, who was delegated to study this request, reviewed the work very favorably as "new proof of the outstanding abilities of the petitioner", who in addition to being a competent theoretician is also a "clever, practical investigator". On June 23, ABELJANZ recommended approval of WERNER's request. As for the *Probevorlesung*, Prof. KLEINER recommended a week later (June 30, *i. e.*, after WERNER's lecture of June 26) that, in view of the candidate's "scientific stature", the usual formal lecture before the assembled faculty be dispensed with and that a report of a visit to the candidate's lecture by himself and Prof. HEIM be accepted in its stead. This request, too, was granted.

Finally, on the last day of August, 1893, after all the formalities had been concluded, WERNER was officially appointed as *Ausserordentlicher (Extraordinarius) Professor für organische Chemie* at the *Zürcher Hochschule* for the usual term of six years, with a salary, in addition to *Kollegiengelder*, of Sw. Fr. 2500. He was to be entrusted with "organic chemistry, along with supplementary special lectures, theoretical chemistry, and *Laboratorium A*". *Laboratorium B*, which served medical students and teaching candidates, remained under the supervision of Prof. ABELJANZ, whose lecture assignment included "inorganic chemistry, analytical chemistry, and supplementary lectures".

Thus, with the advent of the winter semester 1893/94 (Oct. 17, 1893 — Mar. 10, 1894) began WERNER's long and distinguished career at *Universität Zürich*. His first course was the chemistry of aromatic compounds. Since, as we have just seen, the coordination theory was instrumental in the appointment of WERNER to the *Extraordinariat*, it is now appropriate for us to examine this revolutionary work in some detail.

Chapter 4

An Ingenious Impudence

An unidentified "northern colleague" of WERNER's once told him that his proposal of the coordination theory had been "an ingenious impudence" *(eine geniale Frechheit) (L 37)*. This phrase is an apt one, for at the time of its inception (received by the journal Dec., 1892; published 1893), the theory was largely without experimental verification. The data cited by WERNER in support of his ideas had been obtained by the painstaking efforts of others, especially of the Danish chemist who was to become his chief scientific adversary, SOPHUS MADS JØRGENSEN (1837—1914) [36], (A 165), Professor of Chemistry at the *Polytekniske Laereanstalt* and *Københavns Universitet.*

And now let us briefly outline these new ideas. In his coordination theory, WERNER discarded the confining rigidities of the KEKULÉ valence theory with its artificial distinction between "valence compounds" and "molecular compounds" in favor of a new and revolutionary, comprehensive approach in which the constitution of metal-ammines, double salts, and hydrates were viewed as logical consequences of a new concept — the coordination number *(Koordinationszahl)*. By use of this unifying concept, he divided metal-ammines into two classes — those with coordination number six and those with coordination number four. For compounds of the first class, he postulated an octahedral configuration and for those of the second class, a square planar or tetrahedral configuration. He then proceeded to demonstrate the correctness of these stereochemical views by citing various reactions, transformations, and cases of isomerism. In this classic paper, WERNER did not limit himself exclusively to the constitution and configuration of "molecular compounds", but he also speculated upon other topics such as the state of metal salts in solution and the polarization effects involved in chemical bonding.

Space limitations do not permit us to consider here the theoretical aspects or practical applications of the coordination theory. For this, a separate volume is necessary. We can, and must, however, examine here the unusual circumstances surrounding the genesis of the theory, for they provide us with a classic example of what ALFRED B. GARRETT has called "the flash of genius" [37]. As such, WERNER's creation of the coordination theory deserves a place in the history of chemistry that ranks with KEKULÉ's dreams [*38*] of the self-linking of carbon atoms (1858) and of the benzene ring (1865).

"The inspiration came to him like a flash," relates PAUL PFEIFFER (*B 30, B 31*), drawing on his many conversations with WERNER. "One morning at two o'clock he awoke with a start: the long-sought solution of this problem had lodged in his brain. He arose from his bed and by five o'clock in the afternoon the essential points of the coordination theory were achieved." The accounts of ROBERT HUBER (*B 12*), WERNER's former student and lecture assistant, and of ROBERT WIZINGER [*4*], a former student of PFEIFFER's, agree with PFEIFFER's tale. WIZINGER also adds that WERNER wrote the paper without interruption, forcibly keeping himself awake with strong coffee.

How can we account for "the flash of genius" that gave birth to this highly original theory? How can we explain the sudden, subconscious, visual illumination experienced late one night in 1892 by a young, relatively inexperienced *Privat-Dozent* slumbering in his bed in the Hotel *Pfauen* in Zürich? How can we analyze the uncanny insight that in one stroke united under one all-encompassing viewpoint a myriad of previously unexplained "molecular compounds"?

The factors involved in creative work have been discussed for thousands of years. The ancient Greeks invoked the Muses to account for the seemingly inexplicable phenomenon. More recently, scholars in many fields of science and the humanities have endeavored to answer questions such as those that we have posed, and a contemporary bibliography of articles and books on creativity would reach impressive proportions [*39*]. However, we have just begun to scratch the surface of this intriguing problem, and much additional work is needed before anything approaching definitive answers can be obtained. We do know, however, that the secret of creativity lies largely in personality traits, habits, and values rather than in conscious cognitive skills, and it is here that we must seek the answers to our questions.

The force of WERNER's complex and often inconsistent personality, of which we can catch only striking glimpses here and there from the limited material available to us, undoubtedly harbors the key to this riddle of the act of creation. Highly ambitious, dauntless in the face of rebuffs and failures, egocentric, imaginative, intuitive, aggressive, passionate, sensitive, impulsive, obsessed with self-imposed tasks — all these traits known to be associated with high creativity could be used in describing WERNER. Add to this a high degree of native intelligence and a childhood spent in an atmosphere of political unrest, rebellion, and resistance to, and criticism of, authority, and we have the highly combustible mixture which ignited in that sudden nocturnal explosion, the creation of the coordination theory. WERNER himself attributed his theory to "a strong feeling of independence, . . . a lack of belief in authority, . . . and an urge toward the truth" (L 37).

According to PASTEUR, "chance favors the prepared mind", so we might do well to try to determine how long WERNER had mulled over in his mind the puzzle of "molecular compounds" before the brilliant systematization of these compounds came to him in one blinding flash of visual insight. Again we turn to PFEIFFER. "When [WERNER], in the course of working out a theoretical-chemical lecture, became absorbed in the prevailing theories of metal-ammonia salts and related compounds, he soon became convinced that conventional valence theory could not completely explain the constitution of these compounds" (B 26). Now we know that WERNER did not begin his teaching career until the summer semester of 1892 (Apr. 19 — Aug. 6), so the lecture cited by PFEIFFER could not have taken place more than a mere six or seven months before the coordination theory was submitted to the Zeitschrift für anorganische Chemie (Dec., 1892). But could WERNER have become interested in metal-ammines before the lecture in question?

Possibly, but not likely. WERNER was trained as an organic chemist. All his previous publications (A 1—A 13), with the exception of one (A 9), deal with strictly organic topics, and there is no indication that he ever evinced anything more than passing interest in the inorganic field. Although it cannot be proved, it is thus extremely likely that WERNER's first interest in inorganic chemistry that was more than superficial arose in connection with his course "Atomlehre" taught during the summer semester of 1892. If, on the contrary, it did not arise until WERNER first taught "Ausgewählte Kapitel der anorganischen Chemie" (winter semester 1892/93 [Oct. 10, 1892 — Mar. 18, 1893]), his achievement is all the more amazing — almost miraculous!

Whereas the question of the exact date of WERNER's first interest in metal-ammines involved considerable speculation, we can answer a related question with a little more certainty. What is the earliest written indication of WERNER's interest in these compounds? For this, we must examine a brief catalog of handwritten notes, dated Feb. 2, 1890, which incidentally gives further evidence of WERNER's systematic and meticulous habits. This catalog begins with the following proclamation: "Every note is to be written in the same sheet format as the present one. Every note is to be provided with the date and a running number. Every note is to be provided with the title, *etc.*, and entered in the catalog."

This is followed by the results of a study "On an Artificial Dye Formed from Hydrazobenzene ... carried out during the long vacation 1889". Eight additional projects (organic, inorganic, and analytical) are listed by title in the catalog, but the actual notes have not been preserved, with one exception — the one that is of interest to us here — "Über Nickelammoniakverbindungen", dated Feb. 19, 1890. This single sheet lists merely the formulas of nine hexammines, tetrammines, triammines, and diammines of nickel (II) salts, together with three literature references. It is not likely that WERNER ever carried out any experimental studies of these compounds, but at least the notes constitute the earliest preserved documentation of his awareness of the existence of metal-ammines, whose chemistry he was destined to revolutionize less than three years later.

Thus we end our speculations concerning the origin of the coordination theory. How, with only a brief acquaintance with the field and with virtually no experimental background, WERNER came upon his amazing insight during that momentous night still remains an unfathomable mystery. Perhaps, after all is said and done, we can only marvel at its genesis and agree with ALBERT EINSTEIN that "imagination is more important than knowledge".

Once again, we shall succumb, as have others, to the irresistible temptation to compare and contrast WERNER with KEKULÉ. Both men, with the intuition of genius, brought order into large fields of chemistry, WERNER into inorganic and KEKULÉ into organic. Whereas KEKULÉ, however, was primarily a strong theorist and made no major contributions as an experimentalist, WERNER was not only the founder of coordination chemistry but was also the greatest experimenter in this field. Almost every aspect of modern coordination chemistry, if traced back far enough in time, leads to some experimental work of ALFRED WERNER.

PFEIFFER (*B 26*) has also contrasted WERNER with EMIL FISCHER (1852—1919) [9], who predeceased him by a few months. Both were tough men, endowed with indefatigable energy, an insatiable thirst for work, and an inborn talent for observation. But whereas FISCHER's experiments were only observations of natural phenomena and he was cautious in his speculations, the motivation for WERNER's life's work was to discover experimental proofs and extensions of his theory.

Theoretical research *vs.* experimental research! Which should rank higher in the scientific hierarchy? The debate continues endlessly, with proponents of each viewpoint advancing argument after argument. There is much to be said for both sides of the controversy. A strong case for the ascendancy of practice over theory could be made of the work of WERNER's great adversary JØRGENSEN [*36*]. All his investigations were made under the guiding star of the now defunct BLOMSTRAND-JØRGENSEN chain theory. Yet the compounds which he first prepared furnished to a large extent the experimental data upon which WERNER based his coordination theory. Indeed, JØRGENSEN's procedures are still used today along with WERNER's in preparing coordination compounds. On the other hand, we have the statement of one of the greatest experimentalists in the organic field, AUGUST WILHELM VON HOFMANN (1818—1892) [*40*]: *"Für den einen Gedanken der Benzoltheorie gebe ich alle meine experimentellen Arbeiten her"* (I would trade all my experimental works for the single idea of the benzene theory).

Theory *vs.* practice! The never-ending debate continues. Yet ALFRED WERNER remains securely above the fray — for he was a master of both.

Chapter 5

But Enough of Theory!

"Doch genug der Theorie! Langsam und nur von ferne folgt der schleppfüßige Versuch dem Fluge leichtbeschwingter Phantasie!" (But enough of theory! Slowly and only at a distance the slow-footed experiment follows the flight of nimble-winged fantasy!) These words were uttered by A. W. VON HOFMANN [*40*] when he first caught an inkling of the work to be done on phosphonium bases. They could just as easily have been uttered by ALFRED WERNER in 1893.

WILHELM OSTWALD (1853—1932) [*41*] has divided scientific geniuses into two types — the classic and the romantic [*42*]. In WERNER's great adversary, S. M. JØRGENSEN [*36*], (*A 165*) we have the embodiment of the classic type — the conservative, slow, and deep-digging completer who produces only after long deliberation and who slowly develops a traditional theory to new consequences.

In WERNER, on the other hand, we seem to have the prototype of the romantic — the liberal, nay radical, impulsive, and brilliant initiator who produces prolifically and easily during his youth. We have already seen in the last few chapters how WERNER expressed original ideas at an age when most scientists are still content to be led step by step by their teachers.

Yet WERNER's personality is too complex and self-contradictory to be accomodated by OSTWALD's oversimplified dichotomy. After giving birth to the coordination theory, the typical romantic genius of the stereotype would have diverted his attention elsewhere and left to others the long and arduous task of accumulating the experimental data necessary for its rigorous proof. But WERNER combined the impulsive, intuitive, and theoretical brilliance of the romantic with the thorough, practical, and experimental persistence of the classicist. Firmly convinced of the correctness of his views, he now devoted the remainder of his career to an unprecedented series of experimental works which explored nearly every conceivable aspect of coordination chemistry and which simultaneously verified his original theory in virtually every particular.

The fruit of this quarter-century's whirlwind of research activity on the part of WERNER and his students is still preserved in a narrow storage room adjoining the *Grosser Hörsaal* at the *Chemisches Institut der Universität Zürich*. Here the browsing visitor can admire the literally thousands of preparations * contained in carefully labelled tubes which are stored in more than a hundred drawers that are housed in a gigantic, heavy, wooden cabinet which reaches almost to the ceiling. Confronted with the physical evidence of an almost superhuman capacity for work, one can only regard it as the achievement of a man obsessed with a dream, the proportions of which we can never fully realize. WERNER, however, explained his accomplishment quite simply and unpretentiously (*L 37*). "I am conscious of having worked quite diligently. But chemical work was always a pleasure for me, and I have experienced the purest pleasures in the laboratory, when on the basis of reflections I arrived at new conclusions which could be confirmed experimentally."

The first experimental work published by WERNER in support of his coordination theory was carried out in collaboration with his friend and former fellow-student,

---

* The present author would estimate that the number of preparations is in excess of 8,000! This immense collection of complexes was exhibited at the *Schweizerische Landesausstellung (Ländi)* (Swiss National Exhibition) held at Berne in 1914.

Arturo Miolati (1869—1956) [23], later Professor of Chemistry at the Universities of Turin and Padua. The research for the first of these works on conductivity (*A 15*) was performed in Hantzsch's laboratory, and the paper constitutes the last article which Werner wrote while at the *Polytechnikum*. Werner particularly treasured his relationship with Miolati and especially their joint works on conductivity. The first edition (1905) of his text "Neuere Anschauungen auf dem Gebiete der anorganischen Chemie" (*T 2*) is "dedicated to his dear friend Herr Prof. Dr. Arthur Miolati in Turin in remembrance of [their] youthful collaboration". It is unfortunate that this collaboration did not continue beyond 1896. Werner often wrote to his friend, urging him to work on this problem or that, but Miolati was engrossed with problems of his own. Perhaps in order to atone for his failure to maintain his side of their correspondence, Miolati frequently sent Werner gift packages of Italian fruit.

In their classic papers (*A 15, A 16, A 35*), Werner and Miolati showed that the molecular conductivities of coordination compounds decreased as successive molecules of ammonia were replaced by anions and that measurements of conductivities could be used to determine the number of ions in complex compounds. They established the complete agreement in magnitude, variation, and pattern between their experimentally measured conductivities and those predicted according to the coordination theory.

Flushed with victory at such experimental successes, Werner, during his early career, consistently underestimated the magnitude of the task remaining before him. "We have definitely clarified the constitution of the complicated metal-ammines," he wrote to a colleague in an unusually elated outburst of optimism. "I am firmly convinced that I will be able to clarify all the cobalt-ammines by the end of this year" (Jan. 14, 1897). A premature and unjustified prediction in view of the fact that he had published only about half a dozen papers on coordination chemistry! More than 140 additional articles were still to flow from his prolific pen. He and his students continued to prepare extensive series of coordination compounds of widely varying types — mononuclear and polynuclear, stereoisomers and structural isomers, with inorganic and organic ligands, monodentate and chelate — all of which lent support to his theory. After a search of fourteen years, Werner finally succeeded in isolating the highly crucial *cis* isomers of simple tetrammines (ammonia-violeo salts) (*A 123*), whose existence was demanded by his theory but not by Jørgensen's. His Danish opponent immediately conceded defeat.

The year 1907 was noteworthy in WERNER's career for two reasons. Not only did he succeed in preparing the long-sought violeo salts, but this year also marked the zenith of his productivity. No fewer than twenty-eight papers bearing his name appeared in that year! "I must search around for a new, larger subject," he wrote to HANTZSCH on Nov. 16, 1908, "for the investigation of the metal-ammines has succeeded to such an extent that I can no longer hope for really new results." Once again, his prediction was incorrect, for his greatest experimental success, the resolution of optically active coordination compounds, still lay in the future.

WERNER's proof of the octahedral configuration for cobalt(III) and similar ions was based upon comparing the number of isomers actually prepared with the number theoretically predicted for different configurations. Of the three likely configurations — hexagonal planar, trigonal prismatic, and octahedral — compounds of type MA_4B_2 and MA_3B_3 should each exist in three forms for the first two configurations, but only in two forms for the last configuration. WERNER's success in preparing two but not three isomers for these type compounds does not, however, constitute a conclusive proof, for it could be argued that failure to isolate a third isomer does not necessarily prove its nonexistence.

On the other hand, if it is assumed that bidentate (chelate) groups can span only *cis* (adjacent) positions, then for compounds of type $M(AA)_3$ and related types, only the octahedral configuration leads to the prediction of optical isomers (Plate 7, page 69). After many unsuccessful attempts, WERNER was able finally to resolve coordination compounds — *cis*-chloro- and bromoamminebis(ethylenediamine)-cobalt(III) salts (*A 139*). This classical resolution, carried out in 1911 with WERNER's American *Doktorand*, VICTOR L. KING (1886—1958), was sufficient to prove conclusively the octahedral configuration for cobalt(III). Yet, because of the prevalent view that optical activity was always connected with carbon atoms, a number of WERNER's contemporaries argued that the optical activity of these and the many other mononuclear and polynuclear compounds subsequently resolved by WERNER was somehow due to the organic chelate groups present, even though these symmetrical ligands were all optically inactive. Any vestige of doubt was finally dispelled by WERNER's resolution in 1914 of completely carbon-free compounds, the tris[tetrammine-μ-dihydroxocobalt(III)]cobalt(III) salts [*43*], (*A 164*). The carbon atom had not been able to maintain its monopoly on geometric isomerism. Now the tetrahedron was likewise forced to relinquish its claim to a monopoly on optical isomerism.

Although WERNER's untimely death interrupted a number of unfinished projects, his life's work stands as a complete and highly significant chapter in the history of chemistry. Not only did he succeed in unequivocally proving by twenty-five years of experimental labor the dream theory of his youth, but in the last-mentioned work, he confirmed his long-held view that no fundamental difference exists between organic and inorganic compounds. The last brick in the crumbling wall of separation between inorganic and organic chemistry had been razed. The demolition begun eighty-six years before by FRIEDRICH WÖHLER (1800—1882) with his synthesis of urea from ammonium cyanate [44] had at last been completed by ALFRED WERNER.

Chapter 6

The Dilemma

The state of inorganic chemistry during the latter half of the nineteenth century was undistinguished, compared to that of organic chemistry. Only a few individual figures stood out clearly, notably MOISSAN, RAMSAY, and WERNER — in sharp contrast to the many top rank organic chemists. A long stalemate had resulted from excessive dependence on organic structural concepts. Not until the end of the century, as a consequence of WERNER's work, did inorganic structural chemistry take a profitable direction [45].

The central role played by WERNER during these crucial years and the glowing success of his labors in coordination chemistry sometimes tend to obscure the fact that WERNER, especially during his early years, made many worthwhile contributions to organic chemistry. As we have seen, he was originally called to *Universität Zürich* to teach organic chemistry, and as we shall see, it was not until the winter semester 1902/03 that he was finally assigned the main lecture course in inorganic chemistry, which he continued to teach along with organic chemistry throughout his career. Forty-five of his 174 publications deal with organic themes such as oximes, hydroxamic and hydroximic acids, phenanthrenes, hydroxylamines, azo, azoxy, hydrazo, and nitro compounds, and dyestuffs. His investigations and interpretations *(A 138, A 145)* of the WALDEN inversion [46] are still of value today.

For half a dozen years following his call to the university, then, WERNER's attention was divided between organic and inorganic chemistry. Of his first thirty publications (1890—1896), the organic papers outnumber the inorganic ones by a ratio of two to one. Not until 1898, when his reputation in coordination chemistry had been firmly established, did the number of his inorganic papers (twenty-one) reach that of his organic ones.

It was a time when organic chemistry was in a state of extraordinary development, overshadowing the other fields with its brilliant triumphs. WERNER, attracted by the promise of early fame in organic work, yet now basically drawn to inorganic chemistry, wavered for a time, troubled by ambivalence and plagued with doubts. He often discussed these doubts with his close colleague at the institute, AUGUST BISCHLER [2 (pp. 85—86)], a *Privat-Dozent* almost his own age, who had come to the university at the same time as he had. He undoubtedly also sought advice from his older friends, ALFRED KLEINER [47] and ARNOLD LANG [48], who had been instrumental in bringing WERNER to the university and who continued to befriend the young professor. By advising WERNER to follow the field that most appealed to his intellectual and emotional needs and drives, these men deserve considerable credit for his ultimate choice.

"Several times I was at the point of again turning completely to organic chemistry, a field in which I would certainly receive more recognition with less work," he confided to HANTZSCH in a letter of Nov. 25, 1897. "Again and again I have felt compelled to return to inorganic chemistry, perhaps because I really overestimate the importance of these investigations." By 1899, WERNER had made his decision. "This periodic vacillation is now overcome," he announced to HANTZSCH. "Inorganic chemistry presents me with so many problems whose solutions attract me that I shall definitely take the path in the inorganic direction; also, I hope to be able to achieve more there than in the organic field" (July 12).

Despite his almost total commitment to inorganic chemistry, WERNER continued to enrich the organic literature with twenty-one more papers. Yet he now considered himself an inorganic chemist, and, with the zeal typical of a proselyte, he did everything within his power to advance the cause and status of his newly chosen field. We have already learned of his plans for a purely inorganic journal (p. 12), and he sought every opportunity to urge those already in the field to remain and continue in it.

Even routine letters of congratulation rarely failed to include some inorganic "advertising". "I am convinced that your fine work ['Übungsbeispiele aus der anorganischen Chemie'] will do much to redirect the attention of chemists to the inorganic field," he wrote Prof. H. BILTZ [49] of Kiel on Nov. 14, 1907. "And this seems to me highly necessary, for I am more and more convinced that the further development of chemical knowledge will have to proceed on an inorganic basis." After congratulating a young colleague on his recent call to a university (Nov. 19, 1908), WERNER was quick to interject a few words of caution and admonition. "However, I would much regret it if you could not continue to advance in pure inorganic work in your new position, for qualified investigators are still rare in this field."

But whether WERNER worked in the organic or inorganic area, the governing bodies of the *Universität* felt that he had "completely fulfilled, even exceeded [our] high expectations". Only two years after his appointment, the *Erziehungsrat* concluded that the rank of *Extraordinarius Professor* was not commensurate with his importance, inasmuch as his outstanding qualities, increasingly recognized by prominent European scientists such as EMIL FISCHER and ADOLF VON BAEYER, had already resulted in a call to an important German university.* This call WERNER refused, and in appreciation of this decision as well as in recognition of his outstanding teaching and research activity, on June 8, 1895 he was promoted to *Ordinarius Professor*, his salary was increased to Sw. Fr. 3500, and his teaching duties were enlarged.

Another call, this time from Berne, was refused in 1897 and led to another increase in salary (to Sw. Fr. 5500) and to the first of many promises for improvements in the laboratory facilities. This pattern of a call followed by a salary increase or improvements in the institute was to be repeated many times during WERNER's career as the number of tempting offers multiplied — Vienna (1900), Basel (1902), *Eidgenössisches Polytechnikum* (1905), and Würzburg (1910). At the same time, he was awarded numerous honorary memberships and degrees by European and American universities and scientific societies (see pp. 120—122 for list).

The young chemist's growing fame was shown in many other ways. Beginning with 1901, he was asked by the editors of various journals and handbooks to share his encyclopedic knowledge of the literature with their readers. His reviews included

---

* The university is not identified in (*B 33*, June 8, 1895).

articles on both organic (*R 2—R 7, R 9, R 12, R 13, R 16*) and inorganic (*R 1, R 8, R 10, R 11, R 14, R 15*) topics. He was often called upon to review forthcoming texts and monographs as well as to lecture at numerous meetings both in Switzerland and abroad. In 1913, he was awarded the supreme recognition for his work — the Nobel Prize in chemistry.

Now that we have gained an over-all perspective of WERNER's life, we can indulge in a more leisurely examination of various aspects of his personality and career.

Chapter 7

Home and Family

Not long after "Beitrag zur Konstitution anorganischer Verbindungen" had assured him a reputation as a scientist of some consequence and after his lectures at the *Universität* had proved him to be a professor fulfilling the promising predictions made about him by his teachers, WERNER committed himself to Zürich, in which he now felt thoroughly at home, in two decisive ways: he married a Swiss woman, and less than a month later, on Oct. 24, 1894, having established himself as a person "of blameless reputation and with an annual income of Fr. 4,000", he was granted the rights of local *(Bürgerrecht)* and federal *(Landrecht)* Swiss citizenship. Although it was possible to maintain dual citizenship, WERNER chose to renounce his German citizenship, a not unexpected course of action in view of his antagonism toward Germany.

WERNER's bride of Oct. 1, 1894, EMMA WILHELMINE GIESKER, was the adopted daughter of ERNST AUGUST GIESKER, a Protestant pastor. She was twenty-one (born Dec. 14, 1872 in Zürich-Enge) when she met the young and dashing *Extraordinarius Professor*, while both were out horseback-riding one day. After a brief courtship and engagement of only a few months, the couple were married. WERNER relinquished his room at the Hotel *Pfauen*, and the newlyweds settled in a small apartment at Klosbachstrasse 48, less than a mile from the institute.

One of Frau WERNER's first tasks was to transcribe in her clear, firm hand her new husband's lecture notes, which had heretofore existed mainly in the form of innumerable scraps and bits of paper. These notebooks are still preserved, and perusal shows them to be remarkably free of error when one considers that the writer knew almost nothing of chemistry.

A son, Alfred Albert Julius, nicknamed Fredy, was born on July 22, 1897. WERNER reacted with natural pride to his first born. In order to capture the feats of his "young prince", WERNER took a more active interest in amateur photography. When Fredy was only four years old, his father was already giving him lessons in reading, writing, and mountain-climbing.

The young family soon felt cramped for lack of space, and with the aid of a number of increases in salary granted in recognition of his professional growth WERNER began to have his own house constructed on Mar. 15, 1897. In April of 1898, the three-story dwelling at Freiestrasse 111, not far from the chemical institute, was ready for occupancy; this house was to be WERNER's home until his death. Four years after the move, the WERNERS' second and last child, Johanna Emma Charlotte, was born (Apr. 16, 1902).

The WERNERS lived on the second floor (erster Stock). "Our apartment is superb, and we enjoy a very beautiful view of the city and the Uetliberg," he wrote his mother on June 22, 1898. "The little garden naturally gives me much pleasure, and I have spent quite a bit of money on flowers, etc." A neighbor recalls Prof. WERNER as pleasant and unusually attentive to her when she was a child, never failing to offer a gentle greeting and often bringing her small treats or toys. But when he returned home rather late and somewhat unsteady after a sociable evening with friends at the Seehof, tenants would often worry that he might start a fire by turning off the hall gaslights improperly.

Unfortunately but perhaps inevitably, WERNER's youthful involvement and pleasure in his home and family were to be displaced by an increasing and intense absorption in his scientific work. As the years passed, the image that we get of WERNER, as described by colleagues, former students, and friends, is that of a man who lived almost exclusively for his science and who slept little; in the evening he was rarely at home but was either at the institute or with his friends in intensely compressed hours of relaxation which involved, at one time or another, chess, billiards, bowling, and the Swiss national card game of Jass. Most pathetic of all was his increasing and well-known dependence on alcohol, which WERNER, with his characteristic truthfulness, was the first to admit. To quote Prof. Kasimir Fajans,* who studied in Zürich from November, 1909 to May, 1910, "A special recollection in connection with this [lecture of Werner's on stereochemistry] was a remark of Werner's which seemed to be a jest at the time but which later revealed its tragic meaning. Werner said that such fortunate ideas now came to him only under the influence of alcohol."

Inevitably too, Emma Werner's increasing preoccupation with her home and children, an absorption fostered by the *Kinder-Küche-Kirche* tradition of Protestant Zürich, contributed to Werner's alienation from his home. As Werner's horizon expanded and as his professional stature increased, his wife was becoming more and more absorbed in the minutiae of housekeeping. She abandoned her early interest in painting and other extrafamilial activities. In addition, contemporaries report that the pair were quite different in terms of personality; socially, Frau Werner was quiet, somewhat withdrawn, and not nearly as adept as her extroverted, jovial husband, who in this area too was as intense, skillful, and energetic as he was about everything that he enjoyed.

All of the family survived Alfred Werner by many years. Fredy studied medicine at *Universität Zürich* and spent eight years with the Zürich *Kantonspital* until he entered private practice in dermatology in Zürich in 1930. For the first six years of his practice, his sister Charlotte served as his secretary and x-ray technician. He died in Zürich on Dec. 18, 1954, survived by his wife (Erika Mercedes) Lola, née Terlinden, whom he had married on Aug. 17, 1942. Emma Werner passed away on Apr. 15, 1962, cared for until the end by her daughter, who had faithfully devoted herself to this task since her father's death more than forty years before.

Chapter 8

The Institutes — Old and New

When Werner came to the *Universität*, its Chemical Institute was housed in the old building at Rämistrasse 85, which had served as the Chemical Institute of the *Polytechnikum* until the latter had been moved into new facilities at Universität-

---

* Personal communication, Oct. 14, 1963.

strasse 6 in 1887. The building, which was torn down after the erection of WERNER's new institute in 1909, was located on the Rämistrasse side of the main building of the *Polytechnikum*. Today, few of the thousands of pedestrians who daily traverse the broad sidewalk along the western side of the Rämistrasse in front of the *ETH Hauptgebäude* realize that they are treading the very ground on which Switzerland's first Nobel Prize winner in chemistry worked.

Although considered ideal at the beginning of the 1860's, the building, which also housed the chemical laboratories of the *Kantonsschule*, the *Kantonschemiker*, and the Hygiene and Pharmacology Institutes of the university, proved inadequate even during VICTOR MEYER's tenure. The laboratories were much too small to accommodate the burgeoning enrollment and were completely incapable of meeting the technical and sanitary demands placed upon them [2], (B 17, B 32).

The existing conditions would have daunted many a scholar and teacher. As many as 250 students crowded daily into a lecture hall intended for less than 130 listeners. They sat even in the aisles, in the window niches, and in the area surrounding the demonstration table. Note-taking was virtually impossible, and on hot summer days, students sometimes fainted. There was a constant fear of a catastrophe in the form of a fire or explosion.

In the laboratories, conditions were even worse. Only Prof. ABELJANZ's analytical section was housed in reasonably adequate quarters. The other students worked in what they aptly nicknamed the "Catacombs" *(Katakomben)* — unfinished cellars and storage rooms for wood, so poorly illuminated that artificial gas lighting was required even at noon (Plate 1, page 65). The unhealthy contrast of steam pipes overhead and cold cement floors below, along with the penetrating reek of pyridine (there was no ventilation to speak of) completed the dismal scene.

A would-be satirist of the time in a 1900 *Weihnachtskommers** pamphlet announced "a new triumph in Goethe research", claiming that inspiration for the

---

* These chemistry student magazines, issued annually in connection with the traditional Christmas party, although invariably loaded with sophomoric exaggeration, still provide a lively glimpse of the *esprit de corps* of WERNER's students as well as graphic descriptions of institute conditions at the time.

great German dramatist's lines 398—409 of Faust, Part I, came from a visit to the *Universitäts-Laboratorium:*

> "Ah, me! this dungeon still I see,
> This drear, accursed masonry,
> Where even the welcome daylight strains
> But duskly through the painted * panes,
> Hemmed in by many a toppling heap
> Of books worm-eaten, gray with dust,
> Which to the vaulted ceiling creep,
> Against the smoky papers thrust, —
> With glasses, boxes, round me stacked,
> And instruments together hurled,
> Ancestral lumber, stuffed and packed —
> Such is my world: and what a world!"
>
> (Bayard Taylor translation)

Yet HELMHOLTZ's dictum that "the best works come out of the worst laboratories" may have some degree of validity, for it was in the Catacombs that the major portion of WERNER's life's work was performed. In no way did the substandard conditions seem to dampen the youthful high spirits, dedication, and sense of humor of those to whom WERNER later referred as his "enthusiastic young fighters in the battle for knowledge" (*L 37*).

Many of these students were foreigners, attracted by WERNER's growing international reputation. The Swiss students had at their disposal the excellent facilities of the *Polytechnikum,* and quite understandably, few chose to work at the university laboratories. Much of the early research, WERNER admits, could not have been accomplished without the dedicated participation of students, many of them women,** who flocked to the institute from all parts of the world—Germany,

---

* In the *Weihnachtskommers* version, the word *beschmutzte* (dirty) has been substituted for the original *gemalte* (painted) on line 401.

** Paradoxically, although most Swiss cantons still do not grant suffrage to women, the liberal and progressive *Universität Zürich* has the distinction of being the first European university to admit women students (1840). During the 1870's and 1880's, the term *Zürcher Studentin* became a famous mark of distinction throughout the continent. Until World War I, about two-thirds of the women were medical students, and most of them were Russian.

Russia, Poland, Austria, Hungary, Bohemia, England, Holland, Romania, Bulgaria, and the United States, to mention some of the countries represented. The laboratories were so swamped with Russian students, many of them fleeing the harsh conditions of the Czarist regime, that one *Weihnachtskommers Zeitung* announced that "beginning next semester Prof. NUNWIEGEHTS (How goes it?)* will lecture in Russian. The few students who are not conversant with this language should arrange to take private lessons." The late eminent chemical historian JOHN READ [50], who received his doctorate under WERNER in 1907, described the cosmopolitan atmosphere of WERNER's laboratory as an education in itself (*B 32*).

Year after year, with his characteristic persistence, WERNER continually pressured the Zürich authorities to provide improvements in the laboratory conditions. In every annual report to the *Erziehungsdirektion*, he repeated his urgent requests. He called their attention to "these sad circumstances which place us in an inferior position compared to other Swiss universities" (Jan., 1897), and he assured them that "our laboratory could achieve significantly more if it possessed special facilities where investigations in the fields of electrochemistry, thermochemistry, *etc.* could be carried out" (Feb., 1898). By Nov. 28, 1899, WERNER's discouragement was profound, and he wrote to Vienna, from which he had received an inquiry preparatory to a call, "The chemical laboratory at my disposal here in Zürich is so small and its hygienic conditions are of such a nature that it is my most fervent wish to get out of these cramped and unhealthy conditions, all the more since at present there is no possibility of improvement in the foreseeable future."

However, the physical inadequacies of the old structure and the extremely meager budget allotted to the institute were recognized as early as 1896. On July 6 of that year, Dr. R. BINDSCHEDLER, the owner of a Basel chemical factory who had been carefully following WERNER's contributions to the literature, made an anonymous gift of Sw. Fr. 3000 to the university. The sum was to be used by WERNER over a period of three years as salary for a private research assistant. **

In 1900, along with other concessions offered WERNER in order to deter him from

---

* See footnote * on p. 53.

** Almost sixty years later, another member of the family, Dr. EMIL BINDSCHEDLER of Philadelphia, who had earned his doctorate under WERNER in 1901, established a scholarship fund for needy Swiss chemistry students in WERNER's honor (Sept. 9, 1954).

accepting a generous call to the University of Vienna, the *Kantonschemiker* were moved into their own laboratories, and the vacated space was placed at WERNER's disposal. At the same time, the Zürich authorities definitely established the prospect for a new building although they set no date for its construction. Nevertheless, in lieu of a permanent solution to the problem, temporary emergency measures were employed. Makeshift additions to a part of the hall (*Vestibül*) were made as late as 1905, the year in which funds were at last allocated for a new institute.

Finally, a concrete step toward ameliorating conditions was taken; a commission was appointed to investigate the situation. "Recently, a health commission visited our laboratory," reported a sarcastic *Weihnachtskommers* article. "The air analysis in the upper room was as follows: 50% evaporated acids, 30% ill-smelling preparation odors . . . , 10% cigarette smoke, . . . 5% alcohol smelling like beer barrels, and 5% illuminating gas. The health commission agreed unanimously that this combination was sufficient to send less resistant individuals into the great beyond."

On February 20, 1905, the *Kantonsrat* granted a request of the *Kantonsrätliche Kommission* for Sw. Fr. 1,400,000 to be used in the erection of a new institute, and this request, together with other increases in Zürich's contributions to education, was passed by a vote of 31,436 to 15,193 in a referendum held on June 25 of that year.

WERNER's joy at the decision, understandably, was immense. JOHN READ (*B 32*) recalls how the new institute was the major theme of the 1906 *Weihnachtskommers* held at the *Casino Hottingen* and how WERNER, in top oratorical form, described the wonders of the modern structure as part of his traditional annual speech. "It will have water, air, steam, and vacuum connections, but one more thing will be provided without fail — and that will be connections for — beer!" It need scarcely be added that WERNER sat down amidst a storm of applause, followed by the traditional "rubbing of a salamander", the simultaneous draining of beer steins by the entire company and the subsequent simultaneous crash of the empty steins on the tables.

Initially, the completion of the new building was scheduled for the fall of 1907, but various circumstances prevented the realization of this objective until 1909. For WERNER, the construction period meant innumerable time-consuming consultations and negotiations with officials, architects, plumbers, and carpenters as well as seemingly endless and often disappointing compromises and aggravating delays. Yet the anticipation of the fulfillment of his dreams doubled his capacity for work. As we have already seen, in the year of his highest productivity, 1907, he published twenty-eight papers, among them the one describing his preparation of the missing 1,2-dichlorotetramminecobalt(III) (ammonia-violeo) salts (A 123), whose appearance convinced JØRGENSEN of the correctness of WERNER's views. Yet WERNER complained to HANTZSCH (Mar. 25, 1909), "I shall have to work hard if I am to make up for the great amount of time which I have had to devote to the building of the laboratory within recent semesters. But I am not so old yet, and I hope to start in again with renewed strength to work out the problems whose solutions are still close to my heart."

WERNER's eagerness to leave the old building is reflected in a letter of Feb. 9, 1908 to his friend JAKOB BINDLER in Sumatra. "I hope that we can move into the new institute in the fall, and of course I am very happy finally to get out of the old box *(der alte Kasten)* in which I have already had to work for 15 years."

The new institute, to be located next to the *Kantonsschule* on the south side of the *Spitalwiese,* was to embody the latest in modern facilities and equipment, and with this end in view WERNER made a systematic and detailed study of major European chemical institutes. For example, during June of 1908, as the building neared completion, he and *Kantonsbaumeister* (cantonal architect) HERMANN FIETZ made a week's tour of the laboratories of HABER in Karlsruhe, VON BAEYER in Munich, and GUTBIER, a former WERNER student, in Erlangen in order to inspect their equipment.

Of special interest to WERNER was HABER's liquid air apparatus, for he had long desired such a machine. In fact, he did manage to eke out a special budgetary allocation of Sw. Fr. 7,400 for this item. As all his students testify, WERNER's liquid air demonstration became one of his most striking and popular lectures. To express his thanks for the new institute, he gave such an experimental lecture for the *Hochschulverein* at Rüti in the Zürich Oberland. He took an almost childish delight in freezing mercury into rings, using a piece of lead as a ball, and splintering a rubber hose.

The building was finally completed, and on Jan. 29, 1909, WERNER wrote triumphantly to BINDLER, "The main thing is, it's built and cannot be torn down." On Feb. 27, 1909, WERNER's students began to move their work benches and laboratory equipment into the new building. In one of those petty misunderstandings that sometimes disturb the calm waters of academic life, *Kantons-baumeister* FIETZ complained of their misbehavior, and WERNER quickly sprang to their defense in a four-page reply (Mar. 10, 1909) to the accusation. The letter, in which WERNER agrees to compensate for the minor damages, gives us a glimpse of the jubilant mood at that time of both WERNER and his *Doktoranden*. "As far as the so-called parade is concerned . . . , the students hired four musicians who played a sad farewell to the old building and then, marching in front of the automobile (which brought the things to the new institute), played a gay march. All who witnessed this parade considered it a highly successful student joke. Thus, in this regard too, the severe word 'misbehavior' *(Ungehörigkeit)* can hardly be used." WERNER's statement that as a teacher he always tried "to remember not to squelch the true cheerfulness of youth" *(L 41)* was not just an idle oratorical remark.

WERNER was immensely elated by the completion of the new building, so much so that he could not wait for the official dedication to show it to his colleagues in the *Schweizerische Chemische Gesellschaft*. The impressive winter meeting of the organization, held on Mar. 6, 1909 in the new institute, was attended by many foreign scholars. In addition to playing the part of the proud host and tour guide, WERNER also presented a paper on polynuclear complexes containing tetravalent cobalt *(L 26)*.

Finally Saturday, Apr. 17, 1909, the day of the dedication of the new institute and one of the happiest days in WERNER's life, arrived.* At half past nine on this bright and sunny morning, WERNER rose to welcome the audience in the large auditorium, which was filled to capacity. In places of honor sat the high officials of the *Universität*, the *Polytechnikum*, and *Kanton Zürich*. Former students, friends, and delegates representing many of the major European universities also attended the ceremony. "On the lecture table, among retorts, vials, and experimental glassware, stood a bouquet, donated by Prof. WERNER's feminine alchemists."

After a speech by *Regierungspräsident* HEINRICH ERNST, WERNER's faculty colleague and personal friend Prof. ALFRED KLEINER [47], now *Rektor* of the *Universität*, thanked WERNER for his prominent role in the planning and completion of the building, and he formally accepted it in the name of the

---

* "Einweihungsfeier des neuen chemischen Institutes der Universität Zürich," *Neue Zürcher Zeitung*, No. 107, Sunday, Apr. 18, 1909.

university. WERNER approached the podium, accompanied by a huge ovation. He presented the officials with a *Festschrift* compiled by the students, which summarized the history of the Chemical Institute from 1833 to the present [2]. Then, using a slide projector, he described the building in great detail. * After *Kandidat* ERNST BLATTER, who later received his doctorate under WERNER in 1912, had conveyed the thanks of the students, WERNER led a guided tour of the institute, "from cellar to attic". A banquet at the *Schmiedstube,* attended by 150 persons, completed the formal festivities, but the chemistry students later had their own *Kommers* at the *Korsotheater.*

WERNER was well pleased with the new facilities, among the finest in Europe, for which he had worked and struggled so long. JOHN READ *(B 32)* relates how in 1910 WERNER visited the Würzburg laboratories in connection with the call that he received that year. As he was shown one treasured asset after another, his only reply was a laconic *"Ja. Was haben Sie sonst?"* (Yes. What else have you got?)

A fairly accurate description of the large auditorium, said to be patterned after EMIL FISCHER's in Berlin, is found, strangely enough, in a work of fiction. In one chapter of his novel "Öppi der Student" (Conzett & Huber, Zürich, **1947**), the Zürich author ARNOLD KÜBLER used WERNER as a prototype for his character Prof. ESSOVIER (SO_4). He described the auditorium as follows: "New, in a new house. A steeply inclining semicircular theater, from whose seats everyone could easily look down onto the experiment table. There were, so to speak, only expensive seats. A mighty single window, as high as the hall itself, formed its outer wall.... A large white chart hung as the only decoration on the [south] wall of the lecture hall: System of the Elements, devised by Prof. A. ESSOVIER."

Today the massive stone structure at Rämistrasse 76 still houses the *Chemisches Institut der Universität Zürich.* It stands as a monument to the energy, enthusiasm, and foresight of ALFRED WERNER.

---

* This 8-page description including nine photographs and eight architectural drawings later appeared in print [*51* (pp. 181—184)]. A briefer description can be found in Reference [*33* (p. 784 ff.)].

Chapter 9

In the Lecture Hall

All reports from those who actually heard WERNER lecture during his prime are unanimous in their glowing descriptions. They differ only in their choice of superlatives. Enthralling! Inspiring! Magical! Fascinating! A perfect joy! Although they all emphasize that one must have been present at WERNER's lectures to understand the deep impression that he made on his listeners, we shall at least attempt to give some idea of his oratorical skill.

Dignified in his entrance as well as his exit, WERNER would make his way to the experiment table, a handsome man of heavy build, broad-shouldered and somewhat stocky. "His head was massive and well-formed, with a great width from eye to ear. His features were rather stern, sometimes even grim, in repose, but when in a good mood, a singularly charming smile would sometimes irradiate his face and light up his eyes" (*B 32*). These large, piercing, blue eyes, so well remembered by all who knew him, would fix upon a hapless disturber and command absolute silence with a single glance. A bushy brown mustache completed this picture of mental and physical strength.

His voice has been most often described as sonorous. His delivery was unusually clear, calm, and precise. Its pace was comparatively slow so that his German was easy for even foreign students to follow and for all to transcribe into notes, a quality which surely filled his listeners with gratitude. * His inner warmth, fire, and contagious enthusiasm caught his audience and carried them along with him.

As WERNER's fame as a lecturer spread beyond the confines of *Philosophische Fakultät II* (Mathematics—Natural Science Faculty), students from other disciplines, even those as far afield as theology and law, would attend his lectures, drawn by his magnetic personality. Many of the medical students decided to become chemists. Even the spacious auditorium of the new institute was soon filled to overflowing, and the crowded conditions of the old institute were repeated. In the winter semester 1913/14, during which WERNER received the Nobel Prize,

---

* RICHARD WILLSTÄTTER (1872—1942) [52] ("Aus meinem Leben," p. 159) [53] found the typical Swiss student very demanding. From his professor, the student expected lectures so complete and polished that purchase of a textbook was unnecessary.

336 students, eager to hear WERNER's course on inorganic chemistry, squeezed into an auditorium with a seating capacity of 209. An excerpt from a *Weihnachts-kommers* catechism drolly comments upon the situation.

"Frage: Wann nimmt der Chemiker das Minimum an Volumen ein?
Antwort: In der Vorlesung von Professor Nunwiegehts." *

One of the hallmarks of WERNER's lecture style was his tremendous capacity for visualization. There was nothing abstract about his brand of chemistry; he spoke as one who had actually seen atoms and molecules, and models constituted an integral part of many of his lectures (Plate 7, page 69). Yet he was well aware of the limitations of such devices, and he scorned those who invested models with too great a degree of physical reality. In a letter to HANTZSCH (Nov. 6, 1896), he complained of just such a chemist. "He is such a *Strichchemiker* that you would have to talk forever to make clear to him that atoms are not balls equipped with wires." EMIL FISCHER [9], who presided at a session of the *Gesellschaft Deutscher Naturforschender und Ärzte* (Frankfurt am Main, 1896), at which WERNER spoke on molecular weight, expressed his satisfaction at finally learning how this concept should be presented to students.

Two attributes that WERNER demanded of his students were punctuality and regular attendance. If a student tried to tiptoe into the auditorium after the lecture had begun, WERNER would stop speaking and transfix the latecomer with a cold, disapproving look which followed the embarrassed culprit to his seat. The offense was seldom repeated. Several of WERNER's former students admit being late to or "cutting" various lectures — but never WERNER's!

It was characteristic of WERNER never to demand of others what he did not demand of himself. His first lecture of the day began at 8:15 A. M., and he was always on time, even after the late hours spent with friends at the *Seehof* or *Pfauen*. He never showed any effects of the previous evening's conviviality. The only recorded instance of his being late to a lecture was on the occasion of the first resolution of a coordination compound (*A 139*). In this case the lecture was canceled at the last moment (*B 20*).

A particularly vivid impression was lent to WERNER's lectures by the obvious care and attention to detail with which they had been prepared. This care was

* Question: When does a chemist occupy the minimum volume?
Answer: In Professor NUNWIEGEHTS' lecture.
See footnote * on p. 53.

especially evident in the perfect timing and performance of the demonstrations. Without even a gesture from WERNER, the lecture assistant would go into action at the appropriate moment. Yet on the rare occasions when a demonstration failed, WERNER would proceed with the lecture, calm and with no hint of annoyance. Perhaps he would interject an offhand remark such as "Well, we'll try to show you that another time".

It goes without saying that the position of lecture assistant was a highly demanding one, for WERNER expected no less than perfection. He received it, too, because of the calm, patient, matter-of-fact, but completely inflexible attitude that he adopted toward his assistants. With an intuitive psychological sense for the principles of effective administration, he trusted them to carry out their assignments with a minimum of supervision. They rarely failed him.

Dr. AEGIDIUS TSCHUDI of Glarus (PhD, 1910), who was WERNER's *Vorlesungs-assistent* at the time of the move to the new institute, tells of working late one night, quite worried because he was unable to get the next morning's demonstration to work. Suddenly WERNER opened the door and peered into the preparation room. "*Nun, wie geht's?*"* TSCHUDI explained his difficulties to the *Chef*, whereupon WERNER's only reply was "Don't worry. After all, you have until eight tomorrow morning." The following day, the demonstration was performed perfectly — though probably by a very tired assistant.

WERNER's demonstrations ranged from simple test tube reactions to those involving complicated, elaborate equipment. He particularly enjoyed spectacular explosions, in which he could indulge more freely in the new auditorium; in the lecture theater of the old institute, students in the front row were scarcely a yard from the experiment table. Sometimes as many as ten demonstrations were carried out like clockwork during the course of a single lecture. By allowing reagents to interact to some extent before the lecture hour, even slow organic reactions could be demonstrated. Many quantitative demonstrations, especially those involving volume relationships in gaseous reactions, were employed in developing stoichiometric concepts in the inorganic course. For these, WERNER relied particularly upon HEUMANN's "Anleitung zum Experimentiren bei Vorlesungen über anorganische Chemie" (F. Vieweg & Sohn, Braunschweig, 2nd ed., 1893).

---

* WERNER was particularly addicted to this common expression; one of the nicknames given him by students was Prof. NUNWIEGEHTS.

The design for one of WERNER's favorite demonstrations, the now obsolete BIRKE-LAND-EYDE nitrogen fixation process for the production of nitric acid, was sent to him by his fellow classmate and co-worker, ARTURO MIOLATI [23]. According to Dr. TSCHUDI, who kindly furnished the photograph (Plate 2, page 65), the combustion chamber (1) consisted of a double-walled, water-cooled copper ring closed by a pair of parallel glass panes fastened with iron rings and screws. The high-voltage current (750—1000 v.) from the electrodes (3) was spread out between the windows into an "electrical sun" by the electromagnet (2). Air was introduced below in the chamber. The resulting brown oxides of nitrogen were drawn off into glass cylinder (4) and absorbed by water in the Woulfe bottle (5). The resistance (8) in the pneumatic trough was used to adjust the arc of the flame.

As we have just seen from his choice of demonstrations, WERNER had an abiding interest in industrial processes and felt that his students should have a firsthand acquaintance with the technical aspects of science. Another way in which he accomplished this goal was by the use of plant trips. Two of his favorite places for such visits were the SCHNORF BROTHERS sulfuric acid plant at nearby Uetikon and the BINDSCHEDLER Chemical Factory at Basel.

In the use of humor in his lectures, WERNER was conspicuously sparing, limiting himself to such subtleties as beginning the lecture after the annual *Weihnachts-kommers* with *"Meine Damen und Herren"*, and then quickly correcting himself to his usual *"Meine Herren und Damen"*. However, in his discussion of fermentation in organic chemistry, he listed in detail the various kinds of *Schnaps* that could be made from different fruits — *Kirschwasser, Himbeergeist, Slivovitz, etc.* — and with a merry twinkle in his eye and with the authoritative air of a worldly gourmet, he pronounced each one in turn *"sehr gut"*.

In another organic lecture, while illustrating the homologous difference, he chose a trio of well-known hydroxylic compounds — C_2H_5OH, CH_3OH, and H_2O. Of the first, he said, *"Das ist Weingeist; das ist giftig"* (This is ethyl alcohol; it is poisonous). By deletion of CH_2, he arrived at the second compound. *"Das ist Holzgeist; das ist giftiger"* (This is wood alcohol; it is more poisonous). Removal of another CH_2 brought him to the final compound. After a dramatically effective pause, he concluded, with mock gravity, *"Und das ist Wasser, das giftigste von allen!"* (And this is water, the most poisonous of all!)

WERNER's lecture notes are eclectic in the best sense of the term. His files contain many holograph versions, the bulk of which consist of his own notes, written while he was a student at the *Polytechnikum*. In the final typed versions, these have been transformed and adapted to his own purposes. Like most good teachers, WERNER was continually revising and rearranging his notes, and even the final versions contain marginal additions and alterations. When Dr. TSCHUDI once asked WERNER the purpose of a volume of Goethe on his desk, WERNER answered without hesitation, *"Um meinen Stil zu verbessern"* (To improve my style).

During his quarter-century tenure at *Universität Zürich,* WERNER taught a variety of courses, the most important of which were inorganic and organic chemistry and stereochemistry. Among the laboratory courses which he conducted on a more or less regular basis were a chemical *Praktikum* for advanced students, a chemical *Halbpraktikum* for natural science students, a chemical-analytical *Praktikum* for chemists, a technical-chemical *Praktikum,* a chemical laboratory for beginners and one for advanced students, and electrochemical exercises. His "Lectures and Discussions on Selected Topics in Chemistry" was particularly popular and well attended. Strangely enough, he lectured on his specialty, "The Chemistry of Metal-Ammonia Compounds and of Double Salts", on only three occasions, all early in his career (SS 1894, WS 1897/98, WS 1899/1900).

WERNER's course in inorganic chemistry, which he began teaching in the winter semester of 1902/03, does not seem revolutionary by present-day standards, for it adhered to the traditional dichotomy of theoretical principles followed by a systematic study of the descriptive chemistry of the elements and their compounds. It should be emphasized that it in no way followed the arrangement of WERNER's "Neuere Anschauungen" (*T 2*) (see pp. 83—84).

WERNER fervently agreed with OSTWALD's maxim that chemistry, if it wishes to be a science, must be able to deduce chemical formulae without postulating the existence of atoms. In his discussion of GAY-LUSSAC's law, for example, he assured his audience that "absolutely nothing hypothetical underlies this arrangement". WERNER, of course, observed no sharp line of demarcation between theoretical and descriptive chemistry; he introduced many theoretical concepts in his descriptive lectures. As in his other elementary courses, he did not discuss his own research; in his consideration of hydrides, he proceeded directly from ammonia to phosphine with only the briefest mention of metal-ammines. As texts, WERNER recommended A. F. HOLLEMANN's "Lehrbuch der Chemie" (Band II, Anorganische Chemie, Veit & Co., Leipzig, 1902), H. ERDMANN's "Lehrbuch der anorganischen Chemie" (F. Vieweg & Sohn, Braunschweig, 3rd ed., 1902), RICHTER's "Lehrbuch der anorganischen Chemie" (ed. by H. Klinger, Friedrich Cohen, Bonn, **1897**), W. Ostwald's "Grundlinien der anorganischen Chemie" (W. Engelmann, Leipzig, **1900**), and of course his own "Neuere Anschauungen" (*T 2*), but he cautioned his students, "You will not find the lectures in the order in which they are presented here in any book; the best thing is to copy the lectures."

In keeping with his emphasis on the empirical approach, Werner began his organic course with qualitative and quantitative analysis and their use in the determination of molecular formulas. The subsequent treatment was traditional — saturated and unsaturated hydrocarbons and then substitution products of hydrocarbons (univalent, divalent, and trivalent functions) and polyfunctional compounds. In the second semester of the course (*"Aromatische Chemie"*), Werner utilized a comparative approach (*"Vergleichende Chemie"*), the observation of each individual function in different parent hydrocarbons.

As we might have anticipated, Werner's stereochemistry lectures paralleled his text "Stereochemie" (*T 1*) (see pp. 80—82), or to be more accurate, the reverse was true; the book evolved from his lectures. Despite its popularity or perhaps because of it, in line with the topsy-turvy logic that often motivates students, the course was singled out for special treatment in the *Weihnachtskommers* parody, "Faust — Eine chemische Tragödie" (Dec. 13, 1912). The student, as in the original drama, complains about all his studies to Mephistopheles. He concludes his long recital of grievances and the 9-page play as well with:

> *"Dazu Stereochemie —*
> *Früher brauchte man das nie!*
> *Man muss schaffen wie ein Tier,*
> *Alfred, ach! mir graut vor dir!"* *

The course was also accorded the dubious honor of being the subject of a satirical song *"Die Stereochemie ist des Werners Lust"*, which was sung to the melody of the traditional German folk song *"Das Wandern ist des Müllers Lust"*.

Werner concluded his course with a warning that was also a prediction: "Stereochemistry, especially as it has developed from valence theory, is something

---

* And in addition, stereochemistry —
It's something that ne'er before needed be!
Like dogs we slave before we're through,
Alfred, how terrified I am of you!

quite incomplete and unfinished. In fact, the structural formulas which play such a large role in organic chemistry have found no application at all in the compounds of inorganic chemistry. Completely new viewpoints must be called into play here if we are to gain a picture of these entirely different compounds. And probably many other viewpoints must be incorporated into the field of constitution theory if we are in some way to attain a complete picture of the elements and compounds of organic and inorganic chemistry."

Chapter 10

In Office and Laboratory

A search for information on WERNER's relations with his students immediately uncovers inconsistencies and conflicting testimony. In interpreting the available data, we should take all the stories with a grain of salt and remember that students are often prone to rationalize their own inadequacies by criticizing their teachers.

Especially contradictory are the stories concerning WERNER's behavior during examinations, all of which were, of course, oral. When it came to intellectual weaknesses, WERNER's humor could become grim and even sadistic. A story told by Prof. emeritus (of the ETH) Dr. JOHANN JAKOB,* illustrates this negative side of WERNER's personality as well as WERNER's impulsive and sometimes explosive temper. WERNER began his examination of a woman student with one of his well-known trick questions, "Name the oxides of bromine".** The hapless girl had apparently not been forewarned, for she hesitatingly volunteered the answer,

---

* A former student of WERNER's who wrote a prize-winning essay on the stereochemistry of coordination compounds [54] and was the first recipient of the *Prix Werner* (see pp. 95—96).
** Since WERNER's day, several oxides of bromine have been synthesized and investigated, a fact which seems to lend support to the wisecrack common in academic circles, "Through the years we don't change the questions; we just change the answers."
In all fairness to WERNER, we must mention that he emphasized reasoning ability rather than simple recall of memorized facts *(Buchwissen)*. He apparently used the latter type of question only to get rid of poorer students with a minimum expenditure of time. As JOHN READ so aptly expressed it, "WERNER did not suffer fools gladly" (B 32).

"BrO?" WERNER led her on, deeper into the trap, "*Und?*" She named another, "BrO₂?" "*Und?*" She responded repeatedly to his leading questions (Br_2O_3, Br_2O, *etc.*) until WERNER said, "That's enough," and dismissed her. She emerged radiant from WERNER's office and joyfully told her waiting fellow students that she had passed after being asked only one question, "Name the oxides of bromine". Even after they assured her that she had failed, she would not believe them. She returned and knocked on WERNER's door. Responding to his gruff "*Herein!*", she opened the door and asked, "I did pass, didn't I, Herr Professor?", whereupon WERNER picked up a chair and threw it at her. She closed the door just in time and could hear the chair splintering against its other side.

From a different source, another less violent story. A trembling medical student reported to WERNER for his oral examination. WERNER greeted him, "If you don't know any more than the man who just left, don't even bother to come in!" This opening remark so demoralized the student that he failed the examination.

Such tales were commonly circulated and possibly exaggerated among students and faculty, and WERNER's reputation as a difficult and intimidating examiner, whether justified or not, became rather firmly established. RICHARD WILLSTÄT-TER [53] described his manner of examining students as "*etwas abschreckend*" (somewhat frightening). To some extent, WERNER enjoyed and perhaps possibly encouraged this reputation. He would laugh heartily and take evident delight in watching *Weihnachtskommers* plays which depicted him as terrifying to students ("*Alfred, ach! mir graut vor dir!*") (see p. 56). In Prof. JAKOB's opinion, "*Werner liebte es, gefürchtet zu sein*" (WERNER enjoyed being feared).

Yet the superior, conscientious students found WERNER to be consistently kind, calm, supportive, and quite fair in the questions which he asked. If a trick question came up, it was obvious enough to be easily identified as such by the better students ("What is the phosphorus content of phosgene?"). This view is supported by such former students as PAUL PFEIFFER (PhD, 1898) [2 (pp. 87—95), 3—6], ANNA ELISABETH ERNST (née DORN, PhD, 1905), JOHN READ (PhD, 1907) [50], AEGIDIUS TSCHUDI (PhD, 1910), and PAUL KARRER (PhD, 1911) [1]. All agree that WERNER took his questions from areas which were obviously known to the student and in which the student would be expected to be prepared. When this was not the case, there was usually a good reason. In his autobiography [6 (pp. 16—17)], PAUL PFEIFFER describes just such a case, his doctoral examination, which, incidentally, he passed "*mit Auszeichnung*" (with distinction).

"On the morning of examination day, Prof. WERNER in the institute asked me whether I was well prepared. I answered that he was well informed about my knowledge from our daily conversations, but I unfortunately added that there were extremely boring areas such as, for example, the azo dyestuffs with their large amounts of material to be memorized and with their limited theoretical viewpoints. ... When I complained to Prof. WERNER the next day that he had asked me about azo dyestuffs although he had known that the field did not interest me, he replied that he wanted to show me that until the examination *he* [italics added] was the one to decide what I should know and that now I could decide for myself."

WERNER's ability to remain calm under even the most trying circumstances, a direct contradiction to the mood exhibited in the chair story, as well as his quick and ready repartee is exemplified by the following story related by Prof. ARTHUR GRUMBACH, a close friend of WERNER's son. The incident is perhaps apocryphal but too delightful to omit.

A Polish girl, desperate and vengeful after failing her examination, took a gun, concealed herself in WERNER's garden, and awaited his return. He arrived home. She fired and missed. WERNER calmly turned to her and remarked, "Your aim is no better than your knowledge of chemistry." The *Polizeiinspektorat der Stadt Zürich* reports that neither the *Stadtpolizei* nor the *Kantonspolizei* have any record of the incident. *Se non è vero, è ben trovato!*

In view of the extreme divergence in the picture of WERNER's relations with students, we would do well to consider the alleged incidents in the light of two factors — the type of student involved and the time in WERNER's life when the incident supposedly occurred. We have already shown how WERNER's attitude varied with the ability of the student. As to the second factor, we know that even in his early years WERNER possessed the moody and temperamental nature that we have, rightly or wrongly, come to associate with the artist rather than the scientist.* Particularly in his later years, as his responsibilities increased and his illness caused him immeasurable and untold physical and spiritual anguish, naturally the more impulsive and impatient side of his character came to the fore.

Perhaps WERNER himself best summed up his attitude in describing himself as one who "always preferred to place the factual above the personal" *(immer das*

---

* Surely the coordination theory is as much an esthetic and artistic triumph as a scientific one.

Sachliche über das Persönliche zu stellen trachtete) (*L 41*). His demands on students were based entirely on the demands of the subject matter.* Any consideration of the ability or interest of the student was to him completely beside the point. Perhaps this was one reason why he was unalterably opposed to the introduction of specialized courses in *Didaktik* (educational methods) at the university. Another was probably that he himself taught so naturally that he felt that teaching was not at all something that needed to be or could be taught. And along with this rigid adherence to facts went his uncompromising statement so frightening to many a candidate for an examination, "*Es gibt keine Chemie für Mediziner! Chemie ist Chemie!*" (There is no such thing as chemistry for medical students! Chemistry is chemistry!) (*B 35*).

As for the undergraduate laboratories, WERNER kept close control on these and habitually made the rounds twice a day, once in the morning and once in the afternoon. However, he rarely stopped at the bench of a student; a brief discussion with the young *Assistent* in charge was the limit of WERNER's activity in these laboratories. Prof. PFEIFFER proved to be a more approachable source of information and advice to undergraduates. Most of WERNER's time went to the fantastic number of doctoral candidates doing research under his direction.

The attainment of a doctor's degree at *Universität Zürich* required a difficult course of research and study, but once a student was accepted by WERNER as a *Doktorand,* he, or, as was often the case, she was fairly certain to complete the work successfully. We have already seen how virtually WERNER's entire research career was based on one great intuitive prediction, the validity of which was so firmly established in his mind that he did not hesitate to invest a lifetime of work in proving it. In the same way, a *Doktorand* was never assigned a project until WERNER was certain of its theoretical basis. In addition, its practical feasibility was usually checked in a preliminary way and on a small scale by one of WERNER's *Assistenten* before the problem was actually assigned to a student. Upon the completion of the research, WERNER with his characteristic thoroughness did not merely accept a student's analytical results but had each one routinely repeated by his *Assistent* (quite a job for 25—30 *Doktoranden!*). An unnecessary precaution?

---

* Consider his assignment of the resolution of *trans* isomers to *Doktoranden* without telling them that the task was impossible. Their failures after many attempts, of course, provided a welcome support for the octahedral theory, but could hardly have endeared their mentor to them.

Usually the results agreed, but not always. "I must inform you that your data on disulfocyanodiethylenediamine salts [later published as (*A 51*)] have been examined," WERNER wrote on Oct. 19, 1898 to a *Praktikant* who is best left nameless, "and it has been discovered that they are all incorrect; your so-called scientific investigation is an unheard-of swindle."

With his truly astonishing memory and capacity for work, WERNER would supervise the research of as many as thirty *Doktoranden* at one time, a feat which he continued to perform throughout his active career. His admiring students have related that he maintained a detailed grasp of everyone's research from day to day, and indeed his personal notebook "Übersicht über die Doktorarbeiten" contains simply a list of the students and their assignments; apparently he needed no further mnemonic aids.

As WERNER passed through the laboratory from *Doktorand* to *Doktorand,* his mood would change from mild to stormy, depending mainly upon the ability of the student, but also to some extent on the student's self-confidence. The meek or those unsure of themselves had a difficult time of it with him; those who worked hard, however, and could stand up against his sometimes overbearing and gruff attitude won his respect and admiration. In his impersonal manner, WERNER was very sparing in his praise, but students realized that a compliment from the *Chef* really meant something.

Untidiness infuriated him, especially in later years when he grew less patient and more irritable. The story is told of WERNER's walking by a student's messy work bench and sweeping his arm across glassware, chemicals, and other equipment so that everything was hurled to the floor with a shattering crash. The mood of hushed expectancy and dread which characterized WERNER's laboratory visits is caught in these excerpts from a *Weihnachtskommers* poem ominously entitled "Er kommt" (He's coming):

"Es geht der Alte durch's Labor,	*"Nun räumt noch rasch eure Plätze auf!*
Gefolgt von Dr. Pfeiffer;	*Bigot, es ist höchste Zeit;*
Es schweigen alle Gesänge bald;	*Denn der Herr Professor, ich warne euch,*
Es regt sich ries'ger Eifer.	*Er liebt die Reinlichkeit."**

---

* The Old Man's coming round the class	Now quickly clean your places, do!
With Dr. PFEIFFER following behind.	Heavens, it's almost time,
All songs are quickly stilled, alas,	For the professor, I'm warning you,
Such frantic, busy students you'd rarely find.	Thinks dirt and mess a crime.

In addition to cleanliness, two other qualities that WERNER valued highly were economy and precision, even in the smallest of details. Dr. REINHOLD BÜHLER, WERNER's *Privat-Assistent* in 1918, recalls how WERNER instructed him to strike a match always transversely across the box, never lengthwise, and always perpendicular to the edges, never at an angle, so as to conserve the striking surface!

Perhaps this is an appropriate place to mention the personal technique which WERNER developed in his own individual experimental research. In these days when the trend toward instrumentation is increasing rapidly and when useful but elaborate instruments are in danger of degenerating into status symbols, it should be emphasized that WERNER laid the experimental foundations of coordination chemistry by using the simplest kinds of physical and chemical equipment. Much as a composer may deliberately turn his back on the immense forces of the symphony orchestra in order to work in a more modest medium such as that of a sonata or a string quartet, so did WERNER choose the most elementary, unpretentious, and direct means that would give him the answers that he eagerly desired as quickly as possible.

In his private laboratory, WERNER kept a small experiment table reserved for his personal use. On the table stood several microburners, microfilter supports, and small platinum spatulas, but the majority of the table's surface was covered with what PFEIFFER has described as WERNER's real tools *(eigentliche Arbeitsgeräte)* — small hemispherical glass dishes filled with complexes of all the colors of the rainbow. Although none of these *Schälchen* were labelled, WERNER could immediately identify the contents of each dish even after long periods of absence from the laboratory. His cabinet was likewise filled with hundreds of what appeared to be unidentified preparations with no visible system of arrangement. ERNST BERL (PhD, 1901) [25], WERNER's assistant at the turn of the century, recalls how WERNER became very angry when he attempted to classify the *Schälchen* and bottles; WERNER claimed that he no longer could locate the preparations that he needed (*B 4*).

It was in these *Schälchen* that WERNER, armed with only a platinum spatula and the most primitive of apparatus, subjected the complexes, produced on a larger scale by his assistants, to the most diverse reactions, transformations, and operations. He would qualitatively examine substances by treating small amounts of them on watch glasses with different reagents, using porous clay plates to separate precipitates, and washing these precipitates by moving them with a spatula to a fresh portion of the plate where they were treated with various solvents. To observe WERNER, with his finely-jointed, slim, artistic hands, convert one compound into another or into an entire series of derivatives by this simple method was to realize that one was in the presence of a true master experimentalist (Plate 6, page 69).

A story by NIELS BJERRUM (1879—1958) [55], the famous Danish physical-inorganic chemist, illustrates the speed and efficacy of WERNER's technique [56]. "When I came to Zürich [May-June, 1907] I had a short time before published a paper [57] on a new chromic chloride with only one coordinatively bound chlorine atom $[[Cr(H_2O)_5Cl]Cl_2 \cdot H_2O]$. In order to be able to check this result WERNER asked me to prepare a small amount of it, but instead of carrying out a titration with silver nitrate in order to test it, he only treated a small amount of it on a watch glass with sulfuric acid and in this way prepared a chloridesulfate, which he at once recognized as the so-called Recoura's chlorosulfate $[[Cr(H_2O)_5Cl]$-$SO_4 \cdot H_2O]$. Thus in the course of a few minutes he had acquired the conviction that the substance was really a new monochlorochromic chloride."

In the earlier years of his career, WERNER spent a great deal of time in general scientific discussion, especially on current problems, with his advanced students. Indeed, he organized evening *Colloquia*, which PAUL PFEIFFER remembers for their stimulating and provocative atmosphere. Such discussions were not always easy to follow, for WERNER's encyclopedic knowledge ranged over all of inorganic and organic chemistry, and he often leaped abruptly from one topic to another. In assigning literature references for discussion, he would rely upon his amazing memory and cite authors, journals, volumes, and exact page numbers.

It was quite acceptable to argue with the Master, but one had to be prepared to back up one's statements with one's personal knowledge of chemistry. WERNER became quite annoyed with the citing of mere memorized material *(Buchwissen)* or with arguments based just on quotations of some other scientist's work. He expected critical evaluation and independent judgment from his students. Moreover, with his tremendous capacity for visualization, he scorned the use of the blackboard during these discussions. This taxed his students' intellectual powers to the utmost but sometimes left them far behind and unable to follow his reasoning.

In later years, as the demands of research and administrative duties increased, WERNER was forced virtually to discontinue this type of contact with his students and to rely more and more upon his ever-popular second in command, Prof. PAUL PFEIFFER, to fulfill this function. His discussions with PFEIFFER, however, continued, and a familiar sight in the institute during breaks between lectures was the pair pacing the corridors, intently absorbed in earnest conversation.

Universitäts-Laboratorium A was often likened to a factory, in which dissertations were turned out *en masse* (about two hundred in all), and this prolific productivity was also characteristic of undergraduate degrees as well. For example, even before WERNER's activity was at its height, during the period 1900—1902, fifty diplomas were granted in chemistry, while a total of only forty-five were granted in all of the other fields represented in *Philosophische Fakultät II* combined.

As we have already seen, before assigning a topic to a student, WERNER would have his *Privat-Assistent* carry out preliminary experiments in miniature, and only after he had convinced himself of the practicality of the proposed research did he allow full-scale work to proceed. While one may question the pedagogical value of this procedure, one cannot but admit its efficiency and predictability. Once a student was accepted by WERNER as a *Doktorand,* he knew that his chances of attaining the degree were excellent, although he may have had little choice in his research topic and little opportunity to learn by making his own mistakes.

In this connection, one might also wish to ponder whether it was this high degree of regulation and supervision which may have prevented the formation of a WERNER school in the usual sense of the word. It is true that among his students and one-time associates we encounter the names of academic and industrial researchers such as OSKAR BAUDISCH, ERNST BERL [25], N. COSTACHESCU, WALTER DILTHEY [2 (pp. 96—97)], JEAN V. DUBSKÝ [58], CHARLES GRÄNACHER, ADOLF GRÜN [2 (pp. 98—99)], ALEXANDER GUTBIER [59], HANS VON HALBAN [60], CHARLES H. HERTY [61], GUSTAV JANTSCH, ISRAEL LIFSCHITZ, THOMAS P. MCCUTCHEON, ARTURO MIOLATI (Plate 5, page 68) [23], PAUL PFEIFFER [2 (pp. 87—95), 3—6], ALFRED PIGUET, JOHN READ, ALFRED SCHAARSCHMIDT, YUJI SHIBATA [20], ALFRED SMIRNOFF, EDMUND STIASNY, and even a Nobel Prize winner, PAUL KARRER (Plate 9, page 71) [1], but only a few of these men such as PFEIFFER, GUTBIER, or SHIBATA earned their reputations in the field of coordination chemistry. Perhaps the impact of WERNER's powerful, authoritarian personality and the impression of his control and mastery of his field deterred most of those who had worked with him from any thought of following in his footsteps.

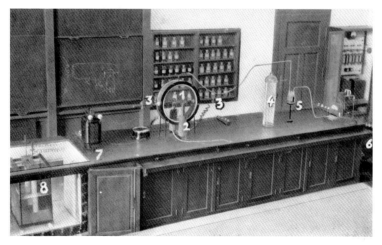

Plate 1. "The Catacombs"

Plate 2. Birkeland-Eyde Nitrogen Fixation Demonstration in the Lecture Auditorium of the New Chemical Institute of *Universität Zürich, ca.* 1910

Plate 3. WERNER as a Student at the *Eidgenössisches Polytechnikum, ca.* 1888

Plate 4. WERNER as a Young *Privat-Dozent*, 1892 or 1893.

Plate 5. Arturo Miolati (l.) and Alfred Werner (r.), Jan. or Feb., 1893

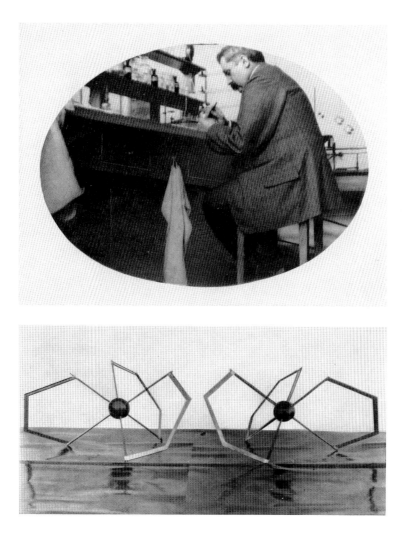

Plate 6. WERNER in the Laboratory (only known photograph)

Plate 7. WERNER's Models of the Enantiomorphs of an Octahedral Trisbidentate Complex

69

Plate 8. ALFRED WERNER and ARTHUR HANTZSCH (1857—1935), Leipzig, Summer 1910

1 PAUL KARRER, PhD, 1911
2 GUSTAV TOEPKE, PhD, 1914
3 FRANZ KLAUS, PhD, 1912
4 SIEGFRIED PRAGER, PhD, 1911
5 ALFRED WERNER
6 HEINRICH SEIBT, PhD, 1913
7 HEDWIG KUH, PhD, 1912
8 SOPHIE MATISSEN, PhD, 1912
9 ALEXANDER FRAENKEL, PhD, 1913
10 CHANA WEIZMANN, PhD, 1912

Plate 9. WERNER with Assistants and Research Workers, 1911 (photograph by Prof. PAUL KARRER)

Hochgeehrte Versammlung,

Wenn ~~alle~~ wissenschaftliche Forscher ~~der~~ ~~für von in die~~ ~~Laboratorien~~ ~~an der~~ Ueberzeugung ~~hat,~~ ~~lebt,~~ dass die Wissenschaft nur ihrer selbst wollen gepflegt ~~werden muss~~ ~~und ~~dass~~ sie~~ jeder ~~Schritt~~ ~~in der Erkenntniss durch~~ ~~machen auch erst~~ ~~vollends~~ nach ~~einer langen, oder~~ ~~später~~ ~~Zeit, das Allgemeinheit~~ in irgend einer Weise zu Gute kommt, ~~bedeutet~~ ~~das~~ ~~ihm volle Befriedigung~~ ~~auch~~ auch dann, wenn ~~auch~~ der äussere Erfolg nicht in dem Maase ~~sich~~ einstellt, ~~wie~~ er zu erwarten sich berechtigt glaubt. Wie ~~viel mehr muss~~ ~~in relativ jungen Jahren~~ ~~das wissenschaftliche Werk~~ ~~preisgekrönt und anerkannt~~ ~~(von~~ ~~den Kompetenteursten~~ ~~die~~ ~~hochangesehenen~~ ~~schafft~~ ~~die Schwedischen Akademie der Wissenschaften.~~

Für Ihre Auszeichnung und für die hohe Ehre, heute vor Ihnen ~~kurz~~ ~~am Bild~~ ~~der~~ in Bezug auf den ~~Bau der~~ ~~Aufbau~~ der ~~der~~ Moleküle ~~erzielten~~ ~~stoffarten~~ ~~Agglomeration~~ erzielten Fortschritte entwickeln zu dürfen, spreche ich Ihnen meinen verbindlichsten Dank aus.

Meine Damen und Herren! Mit ~~einer~~ der Aufstellung einer Hypothese über die Anordnung der Atome in stickstoffhaltigen Molekülen ~~habe~~ habe ich meine wissenschaftlichen Arbeiten begonnen. Die Hypothese hat in der Folgezeit gute Früchte getragen, doch muss ich es mir ~~um so mehr~~ ~~versagen~~ näher auf diese ~~Forschung~~ einzutreten, als ihre experimentelle Bestätigung ihrer Folgerungen noch ~~mehr verbreitet~~ ~~in der hauptsächlich begonnen von~~ ~~durch~~ wenden durch F. Raschig erfolgt ist. Auch auf die kurz ~~so bald nachher~~ in ~~einer~~ der Abhandlung „Beiträge zur Theorie der Affinität und Valenz" entwickelten Vorstellungen möchte ich hier ~~aus~~ ~~kurz hinweisen,~~ denn ~~diese~~ ~~jenen~~ ~~Abhandlung~~ ~~Vorstellungen~~ ~~die darauf abzuleitenden~~ ~~Betrachtungen~~ ~~halten doch im Sinne~~ ~~fortdert~~ ~~den Einfluss auszuüben~~ ~~begannen, der von Ihnen~~ ~~erwarten darf.~~ Ich will mich vielmehr ~~hier~~ ~~darauf~~ ~~beschränken,~~ näher ~~eingehen auf diejenigen meiner Arbeiten, welche~~ sich mit der Konstitution und Konfiguration von Verbindungen befassen, ~~die vor 20 Jahren~~ ~~meist~~ ~~für die~~ ~~nur~~ ~~noch wenig berücksichtigt~~ ~~namlich~~ ~~sogenannten~~ ~~Molekül-~~ verbindungen. ~~Diese~~ ~~Stiefkinder~~ ~~Verbindungen~~ waren ~~während~~ ~~der Fort~~ ~~der großen Entwicklung~~ ~~epoche~~ der organischen Chemie zu Stiefkindern geworden, und

Hochgeehrte Versammlung!

Wenn der wissenschaftliche Forscher in der Überzeugung lebt, daß die Wissenschaft um ihrer selbst willen gepflegt werden muß und daß jeder Fortschritt in der Erkenntnis, wenn vielleicht auch erst in späterer Zeit, der Allgemeinheit in irgendeiner Weise zu Gute kommt, so findet er in seiner Betätigung volle Befriedigung auch dann, wenn sich der äußere Erfolg nicht in dem Maße einstellt, wie er zu erwarten sich berechtigt glaubt. Wie viel mehr muß ich es deshalb schätzen, in relativ jungen Jahren mein wissenschaftliches Werk preisgekrönt und anerkannt zu sehen, von der so hochangesehenen Schwedischen Akademie der Wissenschaften. Für diese Auszeichnung und für die hohe Ehre, heute vor Ihnen ein Bild des in Bezug auf den Bau der Moleküle erzielten Fortschrittes entwickeln zu dürfen, spreche ich Ihnen meinen verbindlichsten Dank aus.

Meine Damen und Herren! Mit der Aufstellung einer Hypothese über die Anordnung der Atome in stickstoffhaltigen Molekülen habe ich meine wissenschaftlichen Arbeiten begonnen. Die Hypothese hat in der Folgezeit gute Früchte getragen, doch muß ich es mir um so mehr versagen, hier näher auf diese Vorstellung einzutreten, als die experimentelle Bestätigung ihrer Folgerungen nicht mein Verdienst, sondern in der Hauptsache desjenige von A. Hantzsch ist. Auf die bald nachher in meiner Abhandlung "Beiträge zur Theorie der Affinität und Valenz" entwickelten Vorstellungen möchte ich hier ebenfalls nur kurz hinweisen, denn die daraus abzuleitenden Schlußfolgerungen beginnen erst jetzt den Einfluß auszuüben, den man von ihnen erwarten darf. Ich will mich hier vielmehr darauf beschränken, näher auf diejenigen meiner Arbeiten einzutreten, welche sich mit der Konstitution und Konfiguration von Verbindungen befassen, die vor 20 Jahren nur noch wenig berücksichtigt wurden, nämlich der sogenannten Molekülverbindungen. Diese Verbindungen waren während der großen Entwicklungsepoche der organischen Chemie zu Stiefkindern geworden, und

Plate 10. First Page of Rough Draft of Nobel Address, "Über die Konstitution und Konfiguration von Verbindungen höherer Ordnung," 1913

Another reason may lie in the thoroughness, breadth, and completeness of WERNER's lifetime of research in coordination chemistry. Indeed, there is scarcely a single aspect of the field, in which he had not performed some experimental or theoretical work. Ironically enough, WERNER's contributions to the field were so enormous and comprehensive that for a number of years many chemists gained the false impression that nothing further remained to be discovered in the area. It is only in the last two decades that this misconception has been overcome and that we have witnessed a resurgence of interest in coordination chemistry. It is unfortunate that WERNER did not live to see this renaissance.

Chapter 11

Der grosse Mann

Even in the early stages of his career at the university, WERNER was regarded by the faculty as *"der grosse Mann"*, an unapproachable celebrity known to all yet really known by none. He is depicted in *Weihnachtskommers* cartoons both as a genius who could put atoms through their paces and as a sphinx — a towering, unshakable, inscrutable figure cloaked in mystery.

ROBERT HUBER (*B 14*) described WERNER's relationships with his colleagues as "good, if somewhat egotistical", but added that "many a person who at first was somewhat repelled by a seemingly rough exterior later accepted WERNER's thoroughly straightforward personality. One always knew where one stood with him, whether in friendship or in anger" (*B 12*).

Indeed, as an example of frankness untempered by tact, it is difficult to imagine anything more characteristic than a letter of WERNER's (Jan. 3, 1899) to another Zürich chemist, who later wrote a book on valence. "Your last expression of opinion convinced me that you are still completely in the dark about the concepts [of] atomic weight and valence, and I can therefore only advise you to choose somewhat simpler problems for your speculations. Please understand that I do not have the time to discuss your peculiar ideas again and again, and I therefore request that you no longer annoy me with this matter since I shall accept no further communications [from you]." The last sentence indicates one reason for WERNER's brusqueness with colleagues and students — lack of time.

In addition to his routine faculty duties of lectures and examinations, WERNER had a lively and genuine interest in university matters and participated regularly and actively in faculty senate sessions. He and his two close friends, Professor of Physics ALFRED KLEINER (1849—1916) [47] and Professor of Zoology ARNOLD LANG (1855—1914) [48], were generally considered the three most powerful men on the faculty. WERNER twice served as Dean *(Dekan)* of *Philosophische Fakultät II* (1902—1904 and 1912—1914) and once as Actuary *(Aktuar)* (1900—1902). His interest in educational matters extended beyond the university, for he served as a member of the *Aufsichtskommission* (supervisory commission) of the *Kantonales Gymnasium*.

In dealing with faculty and cantonal matters, as with his students, WERNER was vigilantly on the side of strict scholastic standards. He did not hesitate to use strong language when it came to criticizing mistakes or negligence. To give one example *(B 4)*, WERNER, at a public lecture of one of his younger colleagues, became convinced that more work was needed on the research being discussed. When the young professor protested that he would not be able to do further work on the problem for another five or six months and that the manuscript had already been sent to *Berichte*, WERNER lost his temper: "You do it, and it makes no difference if you have to work another fifty or sixty years!" Inevitably, such a rough and direct manner aroused hostility and sometimes jealousy. A common rumor, half in jest, half in earnest, was that WERNER's salary was that of six younger professors.

Without a doubt, the man closest to WERNER at the institute was PAUL PFEIFFER, six years his junior, who first came to Zürich in the fall of 1894. Again and again in his autobiography [6], PFEIFFER gives examples of how WERNER's primary interest was in things rather than people — how, as WERNER himself expressed it, he "always preferred to place the factual above the personal" *(L 41)*.

PFEIFFER relates how, as a result of his doctoral research on the highly toxic tin alkyls *(A 45)*, he became very ill and suffered from severe headaches, lack of appetite, double vision, and frequent fainting spells. For a while, it appeared that the illness, diagnosed as retinal inflammation and paralysis of the eye muscle, was going to result in permanent blindness, but after lying in the dark for weeks PFEIFFER slowly recovered. "It struck us as peculiar that Prof. WERNER never visited me during the whole time. To my friend [EDMUND] STIASNY he said that if my condition got worse he would have to look around for another *Assistent* and *Dozent!* He didn't feel at all sorry for me!" *(Mitleid mit mir hatte er nicht!)* (p.16).

As the years passed and his work-load and obligations increased, WERNER came to depend more and more upon PFEIFFER. "My efforts to become STAUDINGER's successor in Karlsruhe [1912] were also in vain," PFEIFFER complains, "mainly because of the slight initiative taken by WERNER, who wanted me to remain in Zürich without fail" (p. 28).

This view of PFEIFFER's that WERNER placed his own need for PFEIFFER above PFEIFFER's own interests is corroborated by an earlier letter of July 9, 1903. In response to a request for his opinion of three candidates (W. MANCHOT, A. GUT-BIER, and PFEIFFER), WERNER described PFEIFFER as "the most qualified of all the young chemists that I know who are working in the inorganic field". With his characteristic frankness, he continued, "But I must add that I would prefer, *in my interest* [WERNER's own emphasis], if on the basis of the opinions that you gather, you would find a more suitable [candidate] than PFEIFFER, much as it would also please me, of course, if PFEIFFER were to take a well-deserved step in his academic career by a call to Würzburg."

As a result of an accumulation of such incidents, PFEIFFER writes, "Unfortunately my relations with WERNER, so good at first, deteriorated more and more as time went by. WERNER simply could not understand that meanwhile I too had become older and more mature and thought differently from him on some chemical problems. In one case he even went so far as to emphasize rather rudely in one publication that my developed concepts — on the WALDEN inversion — were not justified by the facts. He also took a new chemical idea which I had presented to him, developed it himself, and then gave it to one of his *Privat-Assistenten* to work out.* Furthermore, he assigned me only a small room in the new building ... in which I had to work with my assistant; I did not receive an office. For WERNER was by nature a strong egoist, but at the same time a great scholar, whom I admired as before" (pp. 29—30).

At last, the situation became intolerable. PFEIFFER finally realized that he would have to become independent of WERNER if he were ever going to develop his own creative resources. Their relationship was further aggravated by the advent of

---

* PFEIFFER also mentions elsewhere that a scientific idea was taken unfairly from him by WERNER, but it is not clear whether this is the same idea. In any case, the exact nature of the idea or ideas is never described.

World War I; WERNER was, of course, strongly pro-French, and PFEIFFER strongly pro-German. In 1916, although WERNER was already gravely ill and PFEIFFER was certain to be named as his successor, PFEIFFER returned to his fatherland. He accepted a professorship at the *Universität Rostock*.

The WERNER-PFEIFFER relationship, however, never erupted into the kind of open conflict that characterized the relationship between WERNER and ABELJANZ. Although the details of faculty feuds are usually confined to local circles, this story has been widely circulated, as a result of its appearance in WILLSTÄTTER's autobiography "Aus meinem Leben" [*53*]. RICHARD WILLSTÄTTER (1872—1942) [*52*], himself a Nobel laureate, who considered himself a good friend of WERNER's, is generally sympathetic in his treatment of WERNER, yet on p. 169 (German edition), he writes, "The second *Ordinarius Professor* at the *Universität* was ABELJANZ, an Armenian, who of course was poorly regarded by WERNER. For a long time WERNER worked passionately to have him removed and replaced by one of his assistants. It happened that he rushed into the lecture theater after ABELJANZ's lecture and photographed the board with the not too successful formulas and equations in order to provide material proof to accompany his petitions to the administration." Two of WERNER's former students and assistants, PAUL KARRER [*62*] and ROBERT HUBER, immediately refuted the above story, insisting that WERNER would not have been capable of such behavior, yet the rumor persists, especially in Zürich.

The alleged photography incident, if it were true, would have been merely a more dramatic episode in an extended and aggravating conflict between the heads of the joint institutes, a struggle which had begun almost as soon as WERNER joined the *Universität* faculty in 1893.

HARUTHIUN ABELJANZ (1849—1921) [*2* (pp. 47—48), *32*] had studied under BUNSEN, HELMHOLTZ, and KIRCHHOFF at Heidelberg and under WISLICENUS in Zürich. From 1877 to 1884 he served as *Kantonschemiker* for the canton of Zürich. His specialty was chemical analysis, especially of foodstuffs. ABELJANZ's pleasant, cultivated manner, undistinguished scholarship, and twenty years of faculty seniority over WERNER were no match for the latter's gigantic intellect, rough, straightforward, outspoken behavior, and impatience with intellectual limitations. A personal and professional encounter was inevitable.

Despite a series of minor and petty skirmishes, WERNER avoided a direct confrontation until 1900, when the call which he had received from *Universität Wien* strengthened his position to the extent that he felt able to present a list of grievances to the authorities *(Erziehungsrat)* and to demand an end to ABELJANZ's unethical pirating of chemistry students from Institute A "or else". On Dec. 13, 1901, the two adversaries, on their own volition, signed an agreement — or rather, a truce — but it was short-lived.

In the spring of 1902, proceedings were instituted in which ABELJANZ was accused, among other things, of unethical professional behavior, incompetence as a research director (WERNER had directed fifty-six dissertations since 1894; ABELJANZ had directed two), of having produced a poor textbook, and of never having had a worthwhile scientific idea. The official hearings and committee investigations,* which continued through most of 1902, finally resulted in the assignment, effective beginning with the winter semester 1902/03, of both major lectures (inorganic as well as organic) to WERNER, leaving ABELJANZ with only the lecture in analytical chemistry and the laboratory for medical and education students.

One aspect of the conflict has still not been resolved to this writer's satisfaction. The administration's first decision, tantamount to dismissal, was to renew ABELJANZ's position for only one year. Upon petition from the faculty, however, this decree was reversed, and ABELJANZ was rehired for the customary six-year period, with the restrictions noted above. He continued to teach until his death in 1921. Some of WERNER's admirers claim that WERNER was instrumental in preventing ABELJANZ's permanent dismissal, but no conclusive evidence either confirming or denying this claim has been found.

Concerning the genesis of the photography rumor, ROBERT HUBER, who was lecture assistant first to ABELJANZ and then to WERNER during the time in question, has related the facts in an impartial and credible manner.** Photographs of large or complicated apparatus were routinely taken in order to aid subsequent lecture assistants in setting up the demonstrations.*** Two assistants who had failed to complete the doctoral problem assigned them by ABELJANZ noticed a minor error by ABELJANZ (FeS instead of FeS_2) which appeared on the blackboard forming the background in a photograph of apparatus for the preparation of sulfuric acid, and

* *Staatsarchiv Zürich*, M-M 3.16, RRB, 1902, Nos. 518 (Mar. 27), 936 (June 9), and 2551 (Dec. 18).
** Letters to Dr. ANNA ELISABETH ERNST (Mar. 10, 1960) *(B 15)* and Prof. ERNST SCHUMACHER (Oct. 15, 1960) *(B 14)*.
*** The BIRKELAND-EYDE nitrogen fixation apparatus shown in Plate 2, page 65 is a typical example of just such a picture.

they seized this opportunity to give vent to their hostility toward their former mentor. This was how the photographs happened to be used as evidence of habitual errors in the testimony against ABELJANZ, to WERNER's obvious advantage. Whether the story, distorted so as to place WERNER in an unfavorable light, reached Prof. EUGEN BAMBERGER (1857—1932; *Eidg. Poly.*, 1893—1905) [*30*] at the *Polytechnikum* through these same assistants or whether it was passed along by ABELJANZ in a vengeful mood is problematic. In any case, when it reached WILLSTÄTTER, who came to Zürich as BAMBERGER's successor in 1905, it was accepted as truth.

One bitter aftermath of the sordid affair must be mentioned. In the spring of 1903, WERNER was being very favorably considered as a successor to ARTHUR HANTZSCH, who was leaving Würzburg for Leipzig. At the last moment, when news of the call had already appeared in the *Kölnische Volkszeitung* (May 3, 1903) and the *Chemiker-Zeitung* (Vol. **27**, No. 37, p. 446, May 9, 1903), the *Universität Würzburg* administration was apparently influenced to withdraw its offer because of mysterious reports slandering WERNER's character. Documentation on the matter is fragmentary and inconclusive, but it is evident from WERNER's letters of this period that although he knew neither the nature of the accusation nor the name of the slanderer, he suspected, among other things, that the ABELJANZ affair might have been involved. His remarks to HANTZSCH (Aug. 4, 1903), after JULIUS TAFEL had been selected to fill the vacant position, constitute an amazingly apt response to accusations by WILLSTÄTTER and others. "As far as my behavior in the ABELJANZ case is concerned, I am convinced that I behaved as I had to, and if certain persons, without being fully informed of the facts, feel the need to form an unfavorable opinion of me, then they certainly cannot avoid being accused of mischievousness — I doubt that anyone in my position would have acted differently."

It may be mentioned parenthetically that the Würzburg administration subsequently revised their opinion and in June or July of 1910 made WERNER a magnificently generous and tempting offer. As a result of extraordinary concessions offered him by the Zürich *Regierungsrat*, WERNER decided to remain in Zürich, a decision that was greeted with thanks and rejoicing by the faculty and with a torchlight procession *(Fackelzug)* by the student body.

Today, except for the rumors mentioned above, no trace of the bitter feud between WERNER and ABELJANZ remains. Busts of both men by the sculptor,

ARTHUR TIGRAN ABELJANZ, son of Haruthiun, repose in solemn dignity at the *Chemisches Institut* of *Universität Zürich* — WERNER's in the lecture auditorium and ABELJANZ's at the first stairway landing.

Chapter 12

Texts and Professional Activities

In the midst of teaching, research, and administrative activities, WERNER still succeeded in producing his two textbooks within the span of a few years. In 1901, he began work on his "Lehrbuch der Stereochemie" (*T 1*), using as a guide his course lectures on that topic. In a letter of Dec. 23 of that year to his publisher, Gustav Fischer Verlag, he cited his reasons for writing such a book, outlined its contents, and estimated that the manuscript of 12 to 14 *Druckbogen*** (proof-sheets) exclusive of formulas would be ready for the printer by July of 1902.

It is a cynical maxim in publishing circles that the publication date of a book is the date from which postponement begins, and WERNER's "Kurzes Lehrbuch" was no exception to this rule. In this case, it was illness that delayed considerably the completion of the manuscript. On his doctor's advice, WERNER ceased work for two months. In a letter of Oct. 1, 1902, he promised his publisher that he would complete the manuscript by New Year's Day if his nerves did not cause another interruption. Again WERNER was being optimistic in his estimation of the time required. Although he spent the entire spring vacation of 1903 writing, it was not until Aug. 11, 1903 that part of the manuscript was finally sent to the publisher. During the writing period, WERNER was twice approached by other publishers with requests to write a stereochemistry text, attesting to an increasing awareness of both a need for such a book and of WERNER's reputation in this field.

By October of 1903, the book was in press, and in June of 1904, review copies of the volume "dedicated in gratitude to [the author's] teacher and friend, Herr Prof. Dr. ARTHUR HANTZSCH in Leipzig" were on their way to the offices of the major journals. Since the work had grown to 474 pages, the initial word "Kurzes"

---

* The book eventually encompassed twenty-eight *Druckbogen* (each sixteen pages).

(Short) was quite logically omitted from the original title. The subject matter of stereochemistry had indeed expanded phenomenally from its humble beginnings with VAN'T HOFF's fourteen-page essay [28], which had appeared only thirty years before.

"I have tried to treat the subject as completely as possible, if only in a cursory manner, and have tried to consider everything which could be useful in evaluating the extensive data and in studying stereochemical theories, " WERNER stated in his preface. The reviewers (T 1 [a] - [i]) uniformly agreed that he had succeeded admirably in attaining his goal and that in so doing he had fulfilled a need in the literature for an up-to-date, comprehensive review of the entire field from a logical and unified point of view. The work is broadly conceived in two parts — (1) stereoisomeric compounds, both optical and geometric (carbon, carbon-nitrogen, nitrogen, sulfur, selenium, tellurium, cobalt, and platinum compounds), and (2) non-isomeric compounds (cyclic compounds, benzene, and stereochemical effects on reactivity).

When one considers how well it was received and how much it was needed, it is difficult to determine why "Stereochemie" was never revised or translated. Certainly, WERNER had hoped for both possibilities. Even before its publication, he had asked his publisher for an interleaved copy so as to facilitate revision for a second edition, and as early as June of 1904 he inquired as to the possibilities for an English translation. In any case, the text has remained an often cited classic in the field and may be profitably consulted even today for a reliable coverage of the organic and inorganic stereochemistry of that period. It is indeed unfortunate that it was overshadowed by the author's more popular "Neuere Anschauungen" of the following year.

A little-known incident in connection with the "Lehrbuch" may serve to illustrate both WERNER's impulsiveness and his fractious temperament. In May of 1907, the British chemist ALFRED W. STEWART [63], who later engaged in a second career as a mystery writer under the *nom de plume* of J. J. CONNINGTON, sent WERNER a copy of his own recently published "Stereochemistry" [64] "with the author's compliments". It was apparently not until 1908, however, when a German translation [65] of STEWART's book appeared, that WERNER actually read the book. His reaction was violent. "In my opinion and that of my colleagues to whom I have shown it, your book is plagiarism such as will probably seldom be found again in the scientific literature. ... I must regard your publication and its translation as an illegal appropriation of my intellectual property. ... I shall publicly express my frank opinion of this plagiarism so that colleagues can form their own opinions of how your Stereochemistry was put together", he wrote to Stewart on Dec. 3, 1908.

For two months, WERNER attempted to elicit support for his litigation from prominent chemists such as Sir WILLIAM RAMSAY [66] and WILHELM OSTWALD [41]. Everyone advised him against such action. WERNER assured RAMSAY that he wanted to be fair to STEWART, but that "on the basis of this compilation [a detailed comparison of both books], I shall be able to prove publicly that about $3/4$ of STEWART's Stereochemistry was taken from my Lehrbuch" (Dec. 8, 1908). In his next letter (Dec. 28, 1908), WERNER told RAMSAY that he intended to seek the opinion of colleagues familiar with the field of stereochemistry. "The opinions received shall then determine my subsequent behavior in the matter." We may safely assume that this advice agreed with RAMSAY's and OSTWALD's, for WERNER never undertook the public action that he had threatened.

As an examination of both texts reveals, STEWART, in view of WERNER's intense activity in the field, had consulted WERNER's original publications and was careful to acknowledge these by citing complete references. The resulting STEWART text could not help but be based largely on WERNER's earlier work.

Two incidents which illustrate very well WERNER's strong sense of propriety and concern for his intellectual property and scientific reputation may be of interest in this context. When Prof. J. HOUBEN of Aachen [67] claimed priority for a hydrocarbon synthesis of WERNER's (A 73), WERNER made a public statement of the facts of the case, which involved an indiscretion on the part of one of WERNER's students (A 75). HOUBEN replied to this the following year [68].

WERNER wrote at least five letters to HOUBEN between December of 1903 and January of 1904. Perhaps still unduly sensitive because of the false slander directed against him in connection with the Würzburg call of the previous summer (see p. 79), he was more concerned with clearing his good name than in establishing priority. He suggested a compromise and even offered to acknowledge HOUBEN's priority if HOUBEN would publicly make clear that he did not accuse WERNER of stealing his ideas.

Our second incident not only illustrates WERNER's concern with priority but also shows his effective use of sarcasm. A Dutch student, after receiving his degree under WERNER's direction, had returned to Holland and had published his research results on his own and without WERNER's permission. "I see from an abstract in the *Centralblatt* that you have published in the *Nederl. Tag. Pharm.* an interesting article in which you develop quite new speculations on relative asymmetry in nitrogen compounds. The abstract of your work interested me all the more since I too have partially developed similar views privately but have as yet not published them. I have also had one of my pupils, *by chance a namesake of yours* [italics added], make experimental contributions to the development of the problem" (Feb. 18, 1898).

WERNER apparently benefited from the experience he gained in writing "Stereochemie", for on Mar. 7, 1904, he promised the publishing firm of Friedrich Vieweg & Sohn a new book to be finished by April of 1905. He met this deadline much more readily than was the case with the first book, and thus only slightly more than a year had elapsed since the publication of "Stereochemie" when the second of WERNER's texts, his *magnum opus* "Neuere Anschauungen auf dem Gebiete der anorganischen Chemie" (*T 2*), appeared.

General recognition of his theories had been coming too slowly, and WERNER, aware that this was to a large extent due to the scattering of his works in various journals, resolved to summarize his views in this comprehensive, systematic book. The 189-page volume, dedicated to MIOLATI, met with immediate success and still remains today as WERNER's most popular and oft-quoted work. In its brilliantly clear organization and wealth of stimulating ideas, it bears the strong personal stamp of the master teacher. Everywhere the encyclopedic array of descriptive facts are subordinated to the overall plan of the great systematizer.

All five editions of the book* bear the motto borrowed from BLOMSTRAND [69 (p. 127)] which succinctly sets forth the task to which WERNER had dedicated himself in his research: "To explain molecular compounds atomistically, *i. e.*, from the saturation capacity of the elements, has become the main problem of modern chemistry."

WERNER's goal in writing "Neuere Anschauungen", however, was much wider. In his own words (Preface, 1st German edition), "The facts of inorganic chemistry more and more persuasively convince us that the valence concepts which we have developed from the constitutional relationships of carbon compounds do not

---

* The English translation (1911) (*T 2* [*b*]) of the 2nd edition (1909) bears the title "New Ideas on Inorganic Chemistry". Actually, WERNER was more modest; "Neuere Anschauungen" should be translated as "New*er* Ideas".

permit us to deduce a satisfactory view of the molecular structure of inorganic compounds. Consequently, attempts to acquire a broader theoretical basis for the theory of the constitution of inorganic compounds by means of an extension of valence theory are multiplying. And it can already be recognized, if only in blurred outline, what form the extended valence theory and the constitutional view of inorganic compounds, which is to lead us to a knowledge of the general linkage laws of the elements, will take. It therefore seems timely to examine closely in connected form the leading viewpoints which are currently significant for the structural and spatial consideration of the molecular structure of inorganic compounds."

With bold, broad strokes WERNER delineates his grand scheme, designed to demonstrate the interrelationships between practically all classes of inorganic compounds. Following a brief treatment of the elements, he considers compounds of the first order in the light of the usual valency rules. The largest section of the book, which constitutes roughly four-fifths of the first edition, describes and explains compounds of higher order (both *Anlagerungsverbindungen* [addition compounds] and *Einlagerungsverbindungen* [intercalation compounds]). In short, all the inorganic topics treated in the usual standard inorganic texts are found in concise and readable form in "Neuere Anschauungen", and the text serves as a perfect introduction to WERNER's theories, not only of coordination chemistry, but of the whole of inorganic chemistry as well.

Perhaps the highest and most consequential tribute that could be paid to this work was made by G. N. LEWIS (1875—1946) [70], one of the leading figures in modern electronic valence theory, who proposed what later became known as the covalent bond. "'Neuere Anschauungen...' marked a new epoch in chemistry; and in attempting to clarify the fundamental ideas of valence, there is no work to which I feel so much personal indebtedness as to this of WERNER's. While some of his theoretical conclusions have not proved convincing, he marshalled in a masterly manner a great array of facts which showed the incongruities into which chemists had been led by the existing structural formulae of inorganic chemistry" [71 (p. 68)].

Considering the quantity and quality of WERNER's work, it is difficult to understand how he found time to participate actively in so many professional and scientific organizations. Only his strong sense of professional responsibility, his pleasure in discussing chemistry, and his fondness for *Geselligkeit* overcame his reluctance to leave his beloved laboratory. Of the numerous scientific societies of which he was a member, three held a special and intimate place in his affections — the *Naturforschende Gesellschaft in Zürich*, the *Schweizerische Naturforschende Gesellschaft*, and the *Schweizerische Chemische Gesellschaft*.

The *Naturforschende Gesellschaft in Zürich* [72], founded in 1746, represented a wide diversity of scientific disciplines, among them anatomy, astronomy, bacteriology, botany, chemistry, geology, mathematics, mineralogy, pathology, physics, physiology, technology, and zoology. WERNER had published his *Habilitationsschrift* in the society's quarterly journal (*A 7*). Through the years, a number of prominent chemists had been elected president of the organization — POMPEJUS A. BOLLEY, JOHANNES WISLICENUS [12], GEORG LUNGE [15, 16], and EMIL BOSSHARD [73]. In addition, two of WERNER's closest personal friends and colleagues, the physicist ALFRED KLEINER (1849—1916) [47] and the zoologist ARNOLD LANG (1855—1914) [48], were presidents during the years 1894—1896 and 1902—1904, respectively. WERNER himself became one of the moving forces of the society. He served as secretary (1894—1899), *Quästor* (questor) and vice-president (1904—1906), president (1906—1908), and *Beisitzer* (committee member) (1908—1910). For many years he was a hard-working member of the library committee.

From WERNER's election as the 98th member of the society on Dec. 5, 1892, his corpulent figure and ubiquitous cigar were a common sight at the semimonthly Monday evening meetings at the *Zunfthaus zur Zimmerleuten* (Carpenters' Guild Hall) on the picturesque, arcaded Limmatquai, which forms the eastern bank of the Limmat as it flows through the heart of downtown Zürich. He was much sought as a speaker for these occasions. In addition to his popular lectures on his special field, he spoke on various aspects of chemistry such as solubility laws (*L 5*), carbides (*L 7*), new elements and the periodic table (*L 10*), and radium and radioactivity (*L 13, R 14*).

The meetings during the first two decades of the twentieth century are still remembered for the high level of the lectures and discussions. In addition to WERNER's lectures on coordination chemistry, other outstanding talks included those by EINSTEIN (relativity, 1911), WILLSTÄTTER [52] (chlorophyll, 1913), and AUGUST PICCARD (airplanes ,1916). On page 43 of his unpublished autobiography [6], PAUL PFEIFFER [2 (pp. 87—95), 3—5] gives some idea of WERNER and WILL-STÄTTER's oratorical talents. "In general, we young Zürich scientists were convinced that we were gifted above the average and probably all had a good career ahead of us; but there were also moments of severe depression, *viz.*, when WILLSTÄTTER and WERNER delivered their masterful lectures at the *Chemische Gesellschaft*. We then realized that we would never attain to these heights. More than once we considered giving up a scientific career and going into industry."

The *Naturforschende Gesellschaft in Zürich* was a cantonal affiliate of the *Schweizerische Naturforschende Gesellschaft (Société Helvétique des Sciences Naturelles)*. On Aug. 1, 1894, WERNER was elected a member of the national organization, and he subsequently presented many papers at its annual summer meetings. At the 82nd annual meeting held at Neuchâtel, the chemistry section decided to form its own chemical society in order to promote closer communication among Swiss chemists and to represent them more effectively abroad [74,75]. WERNER, along with EUGEN BAMBERGER [30] of Zürich and OTTO BILLETER [76] of Neuchâtel, was appointed to study the attendant problems and to draft a set of by-laws. Their proposals were presented and adopted on the morning of Aug. 6, 1901 at the 84th annual meeting at Zofingen.

WERNER was chosen as the first president of the new society, which was named the *Schweizerische Chemische Gesellschaft (Société Suisse de Chimie)*. He also served the organization in many other capacities, and along with PHILIPPE-AUGUSTE GUYE [77] and F. FICHTER he represented it at several of the early meetings of the *Association Internationale des Sociétés Chimiques* (Berlin, Apr. 12, 1912; Brussels, Sept. 19—23, 1913). These were only a few of the many scientific meetings, both national and international, at which WERNER was a speaker, delegate, or participant. A list of his more important lectures is found in the bibliography at the end of this volume.

WERNER assumed an active and prominent role in the creation of *Helvetica Chimica Acta*, a journal whose purpose was to publish the work of Swiss chemists in one of the three national languages (German, French, or Italian) [74, 78]. He served on the committee of the *Schweizerische Chemische Gesellschaft* which in 1917 spearheaded a highly successful financial drive in support of the enterprise. He was also a member of the advisory committee which drew up the regulations for the new journal and was a member of the first editorial committee. In view of all his efforts toward the creation of *Helvetica Chimica Acta*, it is just and fitting that the first article (*A 169*) to appear in the first issue (May 1, 1918) was by ALFRED WERNER.

Chapter 13

Outside the Laboratory

Day in and day out WERNER was the first to appear at the institute in the morning and the last to leave at night. He even worked on Sunday mornings, as did his *Assistenten,* and for many years he rode a bicycle to work both to conserve time and to provide exercise. During summer vacation, he interrupted this almost superhuman schedule for only a few weeks. A short nap in his office at noon was sufficient to allow this veritable powerhouse of a man to recharge his batteries and so maintain his arduous timetable.

> *"Wenn er z. B. im Büro gelesen,*
> *Sonst war das allemal anders gewesen,*
> *Da hörte der hinterste Doktorand,*
> *Wenn der Alte weilte im Traumesland,*
> *Da fegte ein Sturmwind das Treppenhaus auf,*
> *Bis ganz zu oberst ins Dach hinauf,*
> *Daß Fenster klirrten und Tische wankten*
> *Und Türen girrten und Boden schwankten*
> *Und einer meinte, das könne allein*
> *Die Ursache des letzten Erdbebens sein."* *

As relief from the intensely concentrated pressure of his days, WERNER sought refreshment in a variety of social and recreational activities. As we would expect, he entered into these activities with the same fervor that characterized everything he did. Sociability was for him more than just relaxation; it was an essential need.

---

* "Drehen und Spalten: Tragikomisches Volksspiel in einem Akt," Weihnachtskommers der Universitäts-Chemiker, 15. Dezember 1911, Dissert.-Druckerei Gebr. Leemann & Co., Zürich-Selnau, **1911**. This twelve-page play in verse written to celebrate WERNER's sucessful resolution of optically active coordination compounds is, officially speaking, anonymous, but rumor attributes the authorship to Prof. PAUL KARRER [1], who has confessed to its authorship.

When at rest in his office in former days,	From cellar to attic and all about.
Der Alte had quite different ways.	The windows rattled, the tables tottered,
Then the news reached every *Doktorand,*	The doors were creaking, the floor too tottered,
When *der Alte* was in slumberland,	And all who heard the noise would say,
A hurricane seemed to rage throughout,	The last earthquake was caused this way.

"Ich muss das haben" (I must have it). In his earlier years, he enjoyed all the varied aspects of social intercourse. His early notebooks contain long lists of time schedules, entertainment plans, and guest lists for picnics, excursions, and other social events that he was fond of organizing. However, ALFRED WERNER was no social butterfly. In his choice of close friends, he was highly selective, and he felt most comfortable among this circle of friends *(gemütlich im engeren Kreis)*.

In the congenial company of his good friends, among whom ALFRED KLEINER [47], ARNOLD LANG [48], and later the botany professor HANS SCHINZ [79] deserve special mention, WERNER spent many a sociable evening over a few glasses of wine at the *Seehof* or *Pfauen*. At these times, his robust, jovial sense of humor was much in evidence. For example, JOHN READ (*B 32* [p. 269]) relates that a new colleague at the institute was having a difficult time getting on good terms with WERNER. "One evening, however, WERNER came across him in a less conventional environment, seated at a table with a newly-filled *Bierkrug* before him. As WERNER approached, his colleague greeted him with the customary '*Prosit!*' and tossed off the jorum with polished skill at a single draught — '*in einem kräftigen Schluck,*' as he expressed it. WERNER regarded him steadily. 'Come. There's more in you than I thought!' said *der Alte;* and after this chance encounter WERNER's gruffness was replaced by complete amiability."

A weekly meeting with friends for billiards or bowling was traditional with WERNER for many years. *Jass,* the Swiss national card game, or *Skat,* a popular three-handed card game, often provided another favorite evening's entertainment.

Chess was a consuming passion of WERNER's, and many a time he was seen at the *Saffran* until two or three o'clock in the morning, hunched over a chessboard, deeply absorbed in his game. He claimed that chess relaxed him because it used entirely different brain centers from those that he used in his work. An emotional, agressive player, he always played to win. His interest in chess extended to regular and active attendance at meetings of the *Schachgesellschaft Zürich*. On Mar. 4, 1916 he was made an honorary member of the society in recognition of his many years as vice-president. Although he did not participate in intramural contests, at times he joined the Zürich team in tournaments against other cities. He was even reputed to have written a textbook on chess, a rumor which he denied publicly in his 1913 *Fackelzugrede* (*L 37*), saying that he had "always shown only mediocre achievements in this field".

Of WERNER's hobbies, stamp collecting was a major one, which had interested him since boyhood and which offered him some solace in the days of his final illness. During his early years in Zürich, he wrote his parents to save for him the stamps which he used on his letters since they "may have some value later and will certainly give pleasure to my children if I ever have any" (Jan. 28, 1891). He was quick to notice and save new issues, both domestic and foreign. His collection of Swiss stamps was particularly complete and valuable, and he was reputed to have an entire page of *Basler Brieftauben,* a rare issue of 1845!*

As far as outdoor avocations were concerned, WERNER indulged in a number of activities, including, at one time or another, horseback-riding, ice-skating, boating, hiking, mountain-climbing, hunting, gardening, and photography. We have already seen how WERNER met his wife on a horseback-riding excursion.

"There has been a field of marvelous ice here on Lake Zürich," he wrote to his parents in February of 1891, one of those rare years when the lake froze over. "You have no idea what pleasure it is always to keep advancing on this frozen lake without ever arriving at the end." Evidently WERNER was one of those energetic skaters with the endurance to skate the entire length of the lake to Rapperswil in the canton of St. Gallen. Such excursions often terminated with a happy champagne breakfast, thus simultaneously satisfying WERNER's enjoyment of the outdoors, good food and drink, and *Gemütlichkeit.*

Lake Zürich's thirty-four square miles also provide an inviting treat for the boating enthusiast, and on Sunday afternoons the glossy blue surface of the lake is dotted with hundreds of sailboats, the white of whose sails matches that of the clouds drifting lazily across the sky. WERNER's boating excursions on the lake from the docks of the *Seeclub Zürich* along the Mythenquai were confined to his early years. He became an active member of the club in 1891. Eight years later he became a passive member, and in 1909 he finally resigned from the organization.

The WERNER family usually spent a few weeks of the fall vacation at a mountain resort (Gaflei near Vaduz in Liechtenstein was a favorite one) where WERNER could participate in two other sports in which he was avidly interested — hiking and mountain-climbing. In spite of his size, he was remarkably light on his feet. He could cover a kilometer so rapidly that only the fastest and hardiest hiker

---

* According to SCOTT's Standard Catalog (1955 ed., Vol. II), a single one of these stamps is valued at $ 500 (mint) or $ 400 (used).

could keep up with him (*B 38*). Some idea of his fascination with mountain-climbing may be gleaned from a list of desired Christmas gifts *(Wunschzettel)* which he compiled in 1900. Included are binoculars, hobnailed boots, climbing stick, ice axe, and hunting horn. As we have already seen, his enthusiasm for this arduous sport even led him to introduce his children to mountain-climbing at the age of four!

Apparently, hunting did not occupy WERNER extensively until years later, for in a letter of Jan. 29, 1909 he wrote his friend JAKOB BINDLER, "I have lately begun to take up hunting, until now with doubtful success. I never knew until now how fast hares can run. I have shot at several but haven't hit any yet. Nevertheless, I like hunting quite well, especially the *Mittagessen* out in the open, which always tastes very good." WERNER pursued the sport for a number of years, and his Saturdays were usually reserved for hunting on the grounds in Aargau which he and several friends had cooperatively leased. His hunting dogs, Lord, a black and white English setter, and Tell, a long-haired German pointer, were much a part of the WERNER household.

Not all of WERNER's outdoor activities took him away from his home. Gardening remained one of his lifelong interests, as it had been his father's. His friend, the botanist HANS SCHINZ, would often present him with beautiful and rare plants for the small garden at Freiestrasse 111 as well as material for scientific investigations (*e. g.,* leaves for a study of malic acid).

A portrait of WERNER would be incomplete without mentioning that he was a connoisseur of good food and wine. His personally selected wine cellar contained large quantities of fine vintages organized and inventoried as carefully as he planned and conducted his chemical research. The many bottles and barrels rested on shelves which he himself had designed, and they were arranged according to diagrams and records that he kept in a notebook. He did not limit himself to domestic varieties. For example, he ordered chianti in 200-liter barrels directly from Genoa. RICHARD WILLSTÄTTER [52] recalls how dinners at the WERNER house were interspersed with WERNER's numerous descents into his wine cellar and how a friendly rivalry developed between the WERNER and WILLSTÄTTER families as to the length of the evening meals and the number of courses [53].

There is little doubt that the social event which brought WERNER the greatest pleasure of all was the annual Christmas celebration at the institute. We have already had occasion to refer to these variety shows known as *Weihnachts-*

kommerse. Plans for the party were made weeks in advance; ingenious, humorous, and often elaborate skits, lampooning students, professors, and staff alike, were concocted; in the same spirit a special magazine *(Weihnachtskommerszeitung)* was compiled and printed. The scene of the performance, usually a hall reserved in a local restaurant, was appropriately decorated, complete with Christmas tree. Every year, an increasing number of former students would return to participate in the festivities and to pay their respects to the Master, and every year WERNER would traditionally hold forth with humorous oratory. *"Einmal im Monat darf man sich betrinken"* (Once a month it's all right to get drunk) was one of his favorite maxims on these occasions.

On these occasions too, WERNER would laugh as hard as anyone at the satirical performances, in which he himself did not remain unscathed. "I understand young students and enjoy being able to celebrate with them. I just can't imagine a real student who cannot be gay" *(L 37)*. And by his own definition, he himself remained, throughout his career, a "real student" at heart.

Chapter 14

The Prize

On Nov. 12, 1913, WERNER received a terse telegram: "Nobel Prize for chemistry awarded you. Letter follows. — AURIVILLIUS." Through this brief wire from the secretary of *Kungliga Svenska Vetenskapsakademien* (the Royal Swedish Academy of Sciences), WERNER learned that he had become the fourteenth chemist to receive the internationally famous award and the first Swiss chemist to attain this honor. He reacted to this moment of ultimate triumph with typical candor. "I had not completely eliminated the thought that it would come some day, but I hadn't expected it this year." *

Almost instantly, glowing letters and telegrams of congratulations poured in simultaneously from all parts of the world, and the local papers ** outdid

---

* As quoted in an interview in *Stockholms-Tidningen*, Dec. 10, 1913. On the same day, articles about WERNER's arrival in Stockholm also appeared in *Stockholms Dagblad, Dagens Nyheter*, and *Dagen*.

** See, for example, *Neue Zürcher Zeitung*, No. 315, Nov. 13, 1913.

themselves in their praise of the first Nobel laureate from Zürich. Friends, colleagues, co-workers, and students were naturally overjoyed and expressed their pleasure in the colorful, spirited, and eminently proper way in which the burghers of Zürich celebrate such special occasions. When WERNER entered the lecture hall the following morning, his podium was banked with flowers, and the students rose in unison to stamp and cheer for their illustrious professor. In his office, the desk was inundated with flowers. And of course, that *ne plus ultra* of academic honors, a *Fackelzug* (torchlight procession), was immediately planned. These parades were occasions of great pomp and circumstance. The leaders of the student societies rode in carriages drawn by four horses. Lesser members marched alongside, carrying the torches.

This particular procession, which included three bands, left the Utoquai along Lake Zürich at nine o'clock sharp on the evening of Monday, Nov. 24, 1913. * Despite the light rain, which kept extinguishing the torches and which caused the silken flags to hang limply, it crossed the Quai Brücke, and by way of the Bahnhofstrasse, Limmatquai, and Kreuzplatz it made its way to Freiestrasse 111, where WERNER and his family were waiting on the balcony.

A brief speech was made by JULIUS BÜHRER, president of the student *Korporationenverein*, who then presented WERNER with an *Ehrenkranz* (wreath of laurels). WERNER, deeply moved and in an elated, happy, and reminiscent mood, delivered a lengthy speech (*L 37*) which contains one of his infrequent public pronouncements of a personal and intimate nature. He spoke of his teachers and his early student days, of his motivations for doing research, and of his feelings about his students and his adopted land. He closed with a toast to Zürich, which was joyously and resoundingly echoed by his listeners, who were jammed in the street below. The crowd then hurriedly marched to the Hirschengraben, and at the entrance to the Kirchgasse they sang the traditional *"Gaudeamus igitur"* and threw all the torches together. The resulting bonfire concluded one of the many memorable events of that winter of 1913.

More memorable occasions were to follow. On December 5, Prof. and Frau WERNER left Zürich for Copenhagen and Stockholm. They arrived in the Danish capital the following morning on the express train from Gedser. Since WERNER had arrived earlier than expected, no one met his train, a fact that did not disturb

---

* "Fackelzug zu Ehren Professor WERNERS," *Züricher Post*, Nov. 26, 1913.
Also see reference [24 (pp. 279—280)].

him in the least. He found his own way and had already made the acquaintance of Danish beer by the time that Copenhagen chemists arrived at the *Hotel D'Angleterre* to pay him their respects.

By one of those historical accidents which so often render the truth more dramatic than fiction, WERNER's first triumphal lecture after being selected as Nobel Prize winner was held in the city of SOPHUS MADS JØRGENSEN, who had so long and bitterly denounced the coordination theory. From a local newspaper article* as well as from WERNER's holograph draft of his talk, we know that illness prevented JØRGENSEN from attending the lecture which WERNER delivered that Saturday night of December 6 before the *Kemisk Forening* (*L 38*) as well as the subsequent banquet in WERNER's honor. On this occasion, as on many others, WERNER graciously acknowledged his debt to the older man. Perhaps it was just as well that the ailing JØRGENSEN was spared the applause, the toasts, and the ovations with which his compatriots now fêted his former adversary.

It has generally been reported both by word of mouth and in writing that WERNER and JØRGENSEN never met [*36, 56*], (*G 3*). The reason for this widespread belief may lie in the fact that JØRGENSEN definitely did not attend the Copenhagen meeting at which WERNER spoke. Nevertheless, this fact does not preclude the possibility that sometime during his three-day stay in Copenhagen WERNER may have visited JØRGENSEN at the latter's home. ROBERT HUBER has reported (*B 12, B 13*) a personal conversation during which WERNER related that he had definitely taken advantage of the occasion to visit JØRGENSEN, but that JØRGENSEN was so ill and mentally fatigued that it was impossible to carry on a scientific discussion with him.

Prof. and Frau WERNER left Copenhagen on Monday evening, December 8 and arrived in Stockholm on the following morning. Immediately after checking in at the Grand Hotel, they were caught up in the hectic round of official visits, newspaper interviews, receptions, and banquets which constitute the usual treatment accorded Nobel Prize winners. The imposing award ceremony took place in the Grand Hall of the Royal Academy of Music at five o'clock on the afternoon of Dec. 10, 1913, the seventeenth anniversary of the death of ALFRED NOBEL, with members of the nobility and high officials in attendance. After a brief speech by T. NORDSTRÖM, president of the Royal Swedish Academy of

---

* *Politiken*, København, Dec. 7, 1913.

Sciences, in praise of WERNER's achievements, His Royal Highness King GUSTAV V officially presented the chemistry prize to WERNER, who at forty-seven was the youngest of the recipients. WERNER received a gold medal, an elaborate scroll, and the sum of 143,010.89 Swedish Crowns (*ca.* Sw. Fr. 197,000). According to the official certificate, WERNER was awarded the prize "in recognition of his work on the linkage of atoms in molecules, by which he has thrown fresh light on old problems and opened up new fields of research, especially in inorganic chemistry."

The official ceremony ended with the singing of the Swedish national anthem "*Du gamla, du fria, du fjällhöga Nord*" by the entire assembly, and a banquet held in the Grand Hotel at 7 P.M. concluded the day's festivities [*80—82*].

WERNER delivered his Nobel Prize address, "Über die Konstitution und Konfiguration von Verbindungen höherer Ordnung" (*L 39*) the following day, December 11 (Plate 10, page 72). The fifteen-page lecture was and still is considered a model of compressed exposition, summarizing as it does the labor of twenty years and in addition discussing future problems (*L 39* [*f*]). Again, as usual, WERNER was careful to give credit where credit was due, as has been pointed out by one of his former students, CHARLES H. HERTY [*61*]. "It is interesting that this address was made in that part of Europe from whence came at one time such strenuous denunciations of his views, and it is pleasant to note that in his reference to one of the chemists of the northern country, JØRGENSEN, no scars have been left from the bitter controversy which prevailed in the earlier days" (*L 39* [*f*] [*1*]).

On the evening after the address, the WERNERS left for Berlin, but not before having sent a postcard to the children. "We have enjoyed very beautiful days here and shall satisfy your curiosity on our return to Zürich."

Soon after his return, WERNER and his students, in a bit of inspired tomfoolery, concocted a long and intricate song of thirty-two verses called "*Ein Ball der Elemente*" to be sung to the tune of "*Die Vogelhochzeit*". The parody began:

"*In Stockholm in der schönen Stadt*   "*Den einen gab Herrn Werner man,*
Fand Nobelpreisverteilung statt,   *Die andern drei geh'n uns nichts an,*
Viterullala, viterullala, viterullalalala.   *Viterullala . . .*

"*Um ihn zu ehren hielten all'*
Die Elemente einen Ball,
Viterullala . . ."

The song went on at length to describe how the individual elements participated in the ball held in WERNER's honor. One verse, an obvious reference to one of WERNER's favorite lecture demonstrations, is enough to give the flavor of the seemingly interminable queue of verses:

"Dem Zinn, dem war das einerlei,
Das lachte laut mit 'Zinngeschrei', *
Viterullala . . ."

Dr. M. L. SPRITSMAN of Kishinev, one of WERNER's many Russian *Doktoranden*, who participated in this creative effort, still recalls the Master's obvious delight as he added his more mature baritone to the chorus of youthful voices.

The following spring (May 2, 1914), the *Schweizerische Chemische Gesellschaft* held a special meeting at Neuchâtel in honor of WERNER's having been awarded the Nobel Prize [*83*]. Many friends, colleagues, and former students from all over Europe attended the gala occasion, at which WERNER was presented with a plaque bearing his profile by the eminent sculptor JAMES VIBERT. Eulogies were presented by L. PELET, President of the *SCG*, ALBIN HALLER [*84*], of the *Université de Paris*, and EMILIO NOELTING [*8*], Director of the *École de Chimie de Mulhouse*, to whom WERNER had shown his first original chemical paper almost twenty-nine years earlier. A comprehensive review of WERNER's career and work was also given by Prof. F. FICHTER of *Universität Basel*. WERNER himself discussed the results of his latest experiments on the resolution of coordination compounds, with emphasis on the trisoxalato salts of chromium, cobalt, and iridium (*L 42*). He was also able to announce triumphantly his recent resolution of completely inorganic coordination compounds (*A 164*)

$$\left[\text{Co} \left\{ \begin{matrix} \text{OH} \\ \text{OH} \end{matrix} \!\!\! > \text{Co(NH}_3)_4 \right\}_3 \right] \text{X}_6$$

The Sw. Fr. 800 profit from the sale of souvenir plaques bearing the VIBERT likeness of WERNER, together with a gift of Sw. Fr. 500 from WERNER himself, was used by the *SCG* at its winter meeting in Solothurn (Feb. 27, 1915) to establish

---

* In Stockholm, a city both pretty and gay,
Some Nobel Prizes were given away.
One was for WERNER, which makes us proud,
The others we don't care about.

And in his honor gathered all
The elements to hold a ball.
Not caring who was standing by,
Tin gave its loud and lusty cry.

the *Fonds Werner* (Werner Fund) [*74, 85*]. As soon as the interest from this fund amounted to at least Sw. Fr. 200, a prize *(Prix Werner)* and medal were to be awarded to an outstanding young member of the society. On Feb. 26, 1921, Dr. JOHANN JAKOB, Professor of Mineralogy at the ETH and a former student of WERNER's, became the first recipient. The prize is still awarded each year — a perpetual tribute to WERNER's memory.

Chapter 15

The Final Tragedy

In general, the tragic tale of WERNER's final illness is well known. What is not widely known, however, is that this illness was preceded and foreshadowed by definite indications and warnings that might have been heeded by someone less compulsively dedicated to his science. It may come as a real surprise to many who knew him that the man who presented such a vigorous, active, and powerful figure to the outside world suffered from nervous headaches and signs of chronic overwork throughout much of his life. But WERNER was not one to complain or indulge in self-pity. Perhaps if he had moderated his intense activity, perhaps if he had refrained from "burning the candle at both ends" year after year, his life might not have been cut short at the very zenith of his career.

Yet such speculation is pointless. ALFRED WERNER was a true *Arbeitsmensch.* For him, life without a complete and unrestrained pursuit of knowledge would have been no life at all. In a very real sense then, WERNER died a victim of his work.

As early as May 25, 1899, two decades before his death, WERNER confided to his close friend MIOLATI, "At the end of the winter semester, I already felt extraordinarily tired, which was not surprising, considering the constant overcrowding of the laboratory with *Praktikanten* and my consequently increasing work-load. Nevertheless, I had the unfortunate idea not to use the Easter vacation for a rest but instead to catch up with overdue work during this entire time and to prepare no less than twelve papers for publication." No wonder the beginning of that summer semester was very difficult for WERNER and that a severe case of pneumonia complicated by nervous strain led his physician to insist upon a lengthy period of complete rest.

WERNER paid for the folly of his overwork of 1899; with the exception of his last few final years, the year 1900 was the only one in his career in which he did not publish any papers. On Sept. 20, 1900, he wrote to HANTZSCH that he had not worked much that year, for he had suffered a severe attack of whooping cough, his nerves were troubling him, and he had been forced to spend five weeks at a *Kaltwasserheilanstalt* (hydropathic sanatorium). Through 1902, 1903, and 1904, he had to decline offers from publishers and journal editors because of ill health. For example, on Dec. 24, 1903, he resigned from participation in *Chemische Zeitschrift,* citing as reasons his lack of time and his severe nervous headaches. Although his physician attributed these headaches to overwork, WERNER, unwilling to reduce his activities, did not agree with the diagnosis. In the ensuing years, the literature of chemistry was immeasurably enriched, but at a heavy price, which was paid by a doggedly determined man working in the laboratory on the Rämistrasse.

Shortly after he had received the Nobel Prize, the final difficult trial for WERNER and his family began. The dark shadow of the progressive, degenerative, and fatal illness diagnosed as "general arteriosclerosis, especially of the brain" started its inexorable inroads upon a body already weakened by years of overwork and excessive consumption of alcohol. The order of his physician to abstain from his beloved, habitual cigar was only the first and the smallest of the many sacrifices and changes in his way of life that WERNER was called upon to make.

On July 8, 1915, WERNER asked the Zürich *Erziehungsrat* for permission to conclude the summer session early for reasons of poor health. During that year, he was forced to spend some time at a health resort in Tarasp in the mountains of Grisons. Repeatedly during the winter of 1915 and the spring of 1916, he found himself forced to turn over his inorganic lectures to PAUL PFEIFFER. After PFEIFFER left for Rostock in the winter semester of 1916/17, the lectures were given by WERNER's assistant, CARL AGTHE. Almost to the very end, WERNER tenaciously refused to believe in the critical nature of the disease. His indomitable will-power is reflected in the many poignant letters which document the advancing illness.

Apr. 18, 1916 *(Regierungsrat):* "I do not yet feel able to hold this lecture [organic chemistry] since I still suffer from headaches for hours and days at a time. My physician, Dr. GENHART writes. . . . 'It is my opinion that you should give up the entire summer semester [April—July, 1916]. If you will devote yourself entirely to regaining your health and eliminate all pressures, you will recover completely'." WERNER added that he hoped to resume full activity in the fall. PAUL PFEIFFER, and later CARL AGTHE, frequently substituted for him in the organic lectures.

Feb. 5, 1917 *(Erziehungsdirektion):* "Since I am still not yet recovered sufficiently to be able to resume the lectures without danger of a relapse, I find it necessary to ask the *Erziehungsbehörde* for a leave for the summer semester 1917. . . . My physicians unanimously assure me that I shall recover and shall be able to resume my profession, since my present condition is the result of extreme nervousness. . . . [They recommend] complete relaxation and absolute rest. . . . For this purpose I wish to take up a lengthy residence in a sanatorium." In accordance with his physicians' advice, WERNER entered the *Sanatorium La Charmille* at Riehen, a suburb of Basel, while Prof. ABELJANZ temporarily assumed the general supervision of *Abteilung A.*

A letter of June 18, 1917 to CARL AGTHE is especially pathetic. The firm, precise pen strokes of the hale and sturdy Master have been replaced by the wavering script of a man reduced to a feeble shadow of his former self. Yet WERNER optimistically insists that the worst is over and that his recovery is certain. "The entire illness was exhaustion caused by overwork, and since the illness developed slowly, it will also retreat slowly."

During the winter semester 1917/18, WERNER made a valiant attempt to resume his lecture in inorganic chemistry and the directorship of the institute. This last return, heroic and tragic at the same time, could not help but be a time of intense suffering, for however hard WERNER might have tried to suppress the knowledge, he must have realized that his mental faculties were rapidly deteriorating. He would forget the names, not to mention the research, of his *Doktoranden.* His lapses of memory were extremely erratic; in the mornings, he would remember only events of the previous mornings, and in the afternoons, only those of the previous afternoons.

Difficulties in speech and articulation began to appear. He would rehearse each lecture word for word with his assistants, and even then he would at times be unable to complete the actual lecture. An apologetic assistant would have to finish the lecture of the professor who a few short years before had held his crowded audiences spellbound with his famed oratory! We can only imagine how many times VICTOR MEYER's solution to his illness may have crossed WERNER's mind.

Witnessing this gradually increasing incapacity was, of course, most painful to those who had known WERNER at the height of his powers — his *Doktoranden* of longer standing, his colleagues, and his family. But many of the younger students, confronted only with the WERNER of 1917—1918, reacted with the impatient intolerance of youth. Perhaps the cruelest blow of all came on July 24, 1918 when the *Erziehungsrat* received a petition (*B 39*) with forty-two signatures * which began by declaring that the petitioners had "the highest respect" for WERNER as a scientist and scholar, but that "in the interest of their academic careers" they were forced to lodge the following complaints:

"While the lecture was often unclear even during the winter semester 1917/18 and the lecturer was not able to cover his material adequately, these conditions have become even worse during the course of this semester. With increasing frequency, the incorrect statements of one lecture had to be corrected in the following lecture, and often it was impossible for the students to understand the lecture, much less to take orderly notes from the confused, incorrect formulas written on the blackboard. These abuses have already become noticeable during the last examinations. Moreover, it seems out of the question to the undersigned that the lecturer will be able to cover all his material, since at the end of June not even half of the material covered by him in previous years has been laboriously covered. ... We direct this request to you specifically in order to anticipate the disturbing expressions of indignation which unfortunately have already occurred several times." The petition closes with an urgent plea for "an improvement in a situation which has become intolerable".

WERNER's lectures during the summer semester of 1918 proved to be his last. On Aug. 28, 1918, he wrote to the *Regierungsrat*, "I am forced to request a complete leave for the winter semester 1918. I hope to return fully recovered next spring for the summer semester 1919. ... My nerves are not yet in order. Therefore I suffer from very quick exhaustion. ... [My physicians] strongly urge me to take off for a longer period of time and to rest completely if I wish to recover my former vigor and capacity for work. ... I have been working for 25 years without a long vacation, and my body now demands a long and complete rest." As a result of this letter, Prof. PAUL KARRER substituted for WERNER both as head of the institute and as lecturer.

---

* The enrollment in "Organische Chemie" for the summer semester 1918 was 149.

We may assume that WERNER, struggling resolutely against his fate even on his deathbed, never relinquished his faith in his ultimate recovery. This hope remained with him until his illness had advanced so far that he was mentally incapable of himself writing his request to be retired at the end of the summer semester 1919. This sad duty fell to Frau Prof. WERNER on May 6, 1919. Her letter to the *Erziehungsdirektion* was accompanied by a statement from Dr. GENHART. "The illness has unfortunately made such advances that a resumption of his activity at the university is unthinkable." WERNER's retirement became official on Oct. 15, 1919.

Exactly one month later, on Nov. 15, 1919, at *Burghölzli,* a Zürich psychiatric institution, death at last released WERNER from his long physical and mental suffering. His body was cremated, and his ashes now rest in the family plot at *Friedhof Rehalp* in Zürich. The funeral oration delivered at the grave on Nov. 17, 1919 by THEODOR VETTER, *Rektor* of *Universität Zürich,* movingly recalls the cruel and heartbreaking metamorphosis (*B 42*). "Anyone who met him a few months ago was painfully touched by the breakdown of his powers; anyone who had seen him in full activity received the impression of a victorious, inflexible, intellectual fighter for whom no task was too hard, no problem too difficult, before whom all obstacles had to give way. Let us remember this picture of him during this last hour . . . a man with many excellent qualities who conscientiously used his talents in the service of science and teaching. Let us remember this man here and not the frail invalid whom terrible suffering dragged slowly to his death."

Almost half a century has not dimmed the magnitude of WERNER's achievements. In fact, with the perspective of the passing years, we can better appreciate his monumental and revolutionary contributions. Regardless of what the future holds in store for our science, ALFRED WERNER will be remembered not only as the founder of modern inorganic stereochemistry but also as one of the major chemical figures of all time.

References

[1] ISHII, T.: *Kagaku no Ryôiki (J. Japan. Chem.)* 13, 809—815 (1959).

[2] 75 Jahre chemischer Forschung an der Universität Zürich: Festschrift zur Eröffnung des neuen Chemischen Instituts, verfasst von den Studierenden der Chemie, n. d. [Zürich 1909].

[3] OESPER, R.: *J. Chem. Educ.* 28, 62 (1951).

[4] WIZINGER, R.: *Angew. Chem.* 62 A, 201—205 (1950).

[5] — *Helv. Chim. Acta* 36, 2032—2037 (1953).

[6] PFEIFFER, P.: Mein Lebenslauf. Bonn 1947 (unpublished manuscript).

[7] ANSCHÜTZ, R.: August Kekulé. Berlin: Verlag Chemie 1929, 2 vols.; *idem, Z. angew. Chem.* 35, 467 (1922); *idem, Ber.* 36, 4616—4623 (1903), trans. by E. Farber in Great Chemists. Ed. by E. Farber. New York: Interscience Publishers 1961, pp. 697—702; *idem et al., Ber.* 23, 1265—1312 (1890); Benfey, O. T.: *J. Chem. Educ.* 36, 319 (1959).

[8] REVERDIN, F., and A. PICTET: *Helv. Chim. Acta* 6, 110—128 (1923).

[9] FISCHER, E.: Aus meinem Leben. Berlin: Verlag Julius Springer 1921; HELFERICH, B.: *Z. angew. Chem.* 65, 45—52 (1952), trans. by R. E. Oesper in Great Chemists. Ed by E. Farber. New York: Interscience Publishers 1961, pp. 981—995.

[10] FISCHER, E.: *Ber.* 32, 345—504 (1899).

[11] Eidgenössische Technische Hochschule 1855—1955. Zürich: Buchverlag der Neuen Zürcher Zeitung 1955.

[12] *Vierteljahresschr. Naturf. Ges. Zürich* 47, 456 (1902); BECKMANN, E. O.: *Ber.* 37, 4861 (1904); PERKIN, W. H.: *J. Chem. Soc.* 87, 501 (1905).

[13] MEYER, R.: Victor Meyer, Leben und Wirken eines deutschen Chemikers und Naturforschers 1848—1897. Vol. 4 of Grosse Männer, Studien zur Biologie des Genies, herausgegeben von Wilhelm Ostwald. Leipzig: Akademische Verlagsgesellschaft 1917.

[14] LIEBERMANN, C.: *Ber.* 30, 2157—2168 (1897); THORPE, T. E.: *J. Chem. Soc.* 77, 169 (1900); MEYER, R.: *Ber.* 41, 4505—4718 (1908); excerpts from this in English are found in Great Chemists. Ed. by E. Farber. New York: Interscience Publishers 1961, pp. 855—863; LIPPMANN, E. O.: *Chem. Ztg.* 47, 687 (1923); BUGGE, G.: Das Buch der grossen Chemiker. Von Liebig bis Arrhenius. Berlin: Verlag Chemie 1929, Vol. 2, p. 386 *et seq.*

[15] BERL, E.: *Chem. Ztg.* 47, 157—158 (1923).

[16] — *J. Chem. Educ.* 16, 453—460 (1939).

[17] BODENSTEIN, M.: *Z. Elektrochem.* 38, 899—900 (1932).

[18] SCHOLL, R.: Ansprache zu Arthur Hantzschs 70. Geburtstag (7. 3. 1927), gehalten am 1. 3. 1927 im Hörsaal des Universitäts-Laboratoriums zu Leipzig (unpublished manuscript); BURAWOY, A.: *Ber.* 68, 65—68 (1935); HELFERICH, B.: *Ber. Math.-phys. Kl. sächs. Akad. Wiss. Leipzig* 87, 213 (1935); MOORE, T. S.: *J. Chem. Soc.* 1936, 1051—1066; HEIN, F.: *Ber.* 74, 147—163 (1941); WEISSBERGER, A.: In Great Chemists. Ed. by E. Farber. New York: Interscience Publishers 1961, pp. 1067—1083.

[19] GORDIENKO, A.: Untersuchungen über die Beziehungen zwischen Farbe und Konstitution chemischer Verbindungen. 1912; FRENCH, H. S.: The Absorption Spectra of Certain Chromium Salts. 1913; ANGERSTEIN, J.: Über die Absorptionsspektren von Metallammoniaken. 1914; SCHLEICHER, C.: Über Absorptionsspektren von Komplexsalzen. 1921.

[20] SHIBATA, Y.: *Kagaku no Ryôiki (J. Japan. Chem.)* 2, 284—289, 335—340, 396—400 (1948); 3, 2—9 (1949).

[21] PALMAER, W.: In Das Buch der grossen Chemiker. Ed by G. Bugge. Berlin: Verlag Chemie 1929, Vol. 2, pp. 443—462; trans. and abbrev. by R. E. Oesper in Great Chemists. Ed. by E. Farber. New York: Interscience Publishers 1961, pp. 1093—1109.

[22] ARRHENIUS, S.: Theories of Chemistry: Being Lectures delivered at the University of California in Berkeley. London: Longmans, Green, and Co. 1907.

[23] BRAGAGNOLO, G.: *La Chimica e l'Industria* 39, 101—102 (1957); SANDONNINI, C.: *Atti dell' Istituto Veneto di Scienze, Lettere ed Arti*, Parte generale e Atti ufficiali 115, 1—9 (1957).

[24] ERB, H.: Geschichte der Studentenschaft an der Universität Zürich, 1833—1936. Zürich: Verlag Studentenschaft der Universität 1937.

[25] WINNACKER, K.: *Chem.-Ing.-Tech.* 23, 105—106 (1951).

[26] DENIGÈS, G.: *Bull. Soc. pharm. Bordeaux* 57, 166—196 (1919); JUNGFLEISCH, E. C.: *Bull. Soc. Chim. France* 13, I—CCLX (1913); FARBER, E.: In Das Buch der grossen Chemiker. Ed by G. Bugge. Berlin: Verlag Chemie 1929, Vol. 2, pp. 190—199; trans. by D. S. Farber: In Great Chemists. Ed. by E. Farber. New York: Interscience Publishers 1961, pp. 675—685.

[27] LE BEL, J. A.: Sur les relations qui existent entre les formules atomiques des corps organiques, et le pouvoir rotatoire de leurs dissolutions. *Bull. Soc. Chim. France* [2] 22, 337—347 (1874). An English translation appears in Richardson, G. M.: Foundations of Stereochemistry. New York: American Book Co. 1901, pp. 49—59 and in Benfey, O. T.: Classics in the Theory of Chemical Combination. New York: Dover Publications, Inc. 1963, pp. 161—171.

[28] VAN'T HOFF, J. H.: Voorstel tot uitbreiding der tegenwoordig in de scheikunde gebruikte structuurformules in de ruimte; benevens een daarmee samenhangende opmerking omtrent het verband tusschen optisch actief vermogen en chemische constitutie van organische verbindingen. Utrecht: J. Greven 1874, 14 pp.; La Chimie dans l'Espace. Rotterdam: P. M. Bazendijk 1875; Dix Années dans l'Histoire d'une Théorie (2nd ed. of La Chimie dans l'Espace). Rotterdam: P. M. Bazendijk 1887; Chemistry in Space (trans. by J. E. Marsh of Dix Années dans l'Histoire d'une Théorie). Oxford Univ. Press 1891; Die Lagerung der Atome im Raume (trans. by F. Herrmann of La Chimie dans l'Espace). Braunschweig: Vieweg 1887; The Arrangement of Atoms in Space. Trans. by A. Eiloart. New York: Longmans, Green and Co. 1898, with an Appendix: Stereochemistry among Inorganic Substances by A. Werner; Sur les formules de structure dans l'espace. *Archives Néerlandaises des Sciences Exactes et Naturelles* 9, 445—454 (1874). An English translation appears in Richardson, G. M.: Foundations of Stereochemistry. New York: American Book Co. 1901, pp. 37—46 and in Benfey, O. T.: Classics in the Theory of Chemical Combination. New York: Dover Publications, Inc. 1963, pp. 151—160.

[29] MEERWEIN, H.: *Ber.* 72 A, 111—121 (1939); THORPE, J.: *Chem. and Ind.* 1939, 838—840.

[30] BLANGEY, L.: *Helv. Chim. Acta* 16, 644—685 (1933).

[31] MICHAEL, A.: *J. Amer. Chem. Soc.* 42, 1232—1245 (1920).

[32] KARRER, P.: *Jahresbericht Univ. Zürich* 1921—1922, 54—55.

[33] Die Zürcherischen Schulen seit der Regeneration der 1830er Jahre: Festschrift zur Jahrhundertfeier herausgegeben vom Erziehungsrate des Kantons Zürich, Vol. 3: Die Universität Zürich 1833—1933 und ihre Vorläufer. Ed. by E. Gagliardi, H. Nabholz, and J. Strohl. Zürich: Verlag der Erziehungsdirektion 1938.

[34] KÖNIGS, W.: *Ber.* 37, 4417 (1904).

[35] STRAUS, F.: *Ber.* 60 A, 75—132 (1927).

[36] KAUFFMAN, G. B.: *J. Chem. Educ.* **36**, 521—527 (1959), reprinted in Selected Readings in the History of Chemistry. Compiled by A. J. Ihde and W. F. Kieffer. Easton, Pa.: J. Chem. Educ. **1965**, pp. 185—191; *Chymia* **6**, 180—204 (1960).

[37] GARRETT, A. B.: The Flash of Genius. Princeton: D. Van Nostrand Co. **1963**.

[38] SCHULTZ, G.: *Ber.* **23**, 1302—1306 (1890). For English versions see Benfey, O. T.: *J. Chem. Educ.* **35**, 21—23 (1958) (complete) or Japp, F. R.: *J. Chem. Soc.* **73**, 97—138 (1898) (incomplete).

[39] Books of particular interest to scientists might include Roe, A.: The Making of a Scientist. New York: Dodd, Mead and Co. **1953**; Platt, J. R.: The Excitement of Science. Boston: Houghton Mifflin Co. **1962**. Articles of particular interest to chemists might include Benfey, O. T.: *J. Chem. Educ.* **35**, 21—35 (1958); **37**, 467—470 (1960); and Garrett, A. B.: *J. Chem. Educ.* **41**, 479—482 (1964).

[40] LEPSIUS, B., in Bugge, G.: Das Buch der grossen Chemiker. Berlin: Verlag Chemie **1929**, Vol. 2, pp. 136—153. For an English translation by R. E. Oesper, see Great Chemists. Ed. by E. Farber. New York: Interscience Publishers **1961**, pp. 625—640.

[41] OSTWALD, W.: Lebenslinien, eine Selbstbiographie. Berlin: Klasing & Co. **1926—1927**; OSTWALD, G.: Wilhelm Ostwald mein Vater. Stuttgart: Berliner Union **1953**; FARBER, E.: In Great Chemists. Ed. by E. Farber. New York: Interscience Publishers **1961**, pp. 1019—1030.

[42] OSTWALD, W., in Bugge, G.: Das Buch der grossen Chemiker. Berlin: Verlag Chemie **1929**, Vol. 1, p. 405; FARBER, E.: *J. Chem. Educ.* **30**, 600—604 (1953).

[43] KAUFFMAN, G. B., and R. P. PINNELL: *Inorg. Syntheses* **6**, 176—179 (1960).

[44] WÖHLER, F.: *Pogg. Ann. der Physik und Chemie* **12**, 253—256 (1828).

[45] IHDE, A. J.: The Development of Modern Chemistry. New York: Harper and Row **1964**.

[46] WALDEN, P.: *Ber.* **26**, 210 (1893); **28**, 2769 (1895); **29**, 133 (1896); Optische Umkehrerscheinungen (Waldensche Umkehrung). Braunschweig: Vieweg & Sohn **1919**.

[47] STIERLIN, H. H.: *Verhandl. Schweiz. Naturf. Ges.* **98**, 1. Teil, Nekrologe, p. 28 ff. (1916); H[ESCHELER], K.: Jahresbericht der Universität Zürich, 1916/17, p. 51 ff.

[48] HAECKEL, E., K. HESCHELER, and H. EISIG: Aus dem Leben und Wirken von Arnold Lang. Jena: Gustav Fischer **1916**; HESCHELER, K.: Jahresbericht der Universität Zürich 1914/15, p. 45 ff.

[49] WILKE-DÖRFURT, E.: *Z. angew. Chem.* **38**, 457—458 (1925).

[50] OESPER, R. E.: *J. Chem. Educ.* **26**, 172—173 (1949).

[51] Universität Zürich Festschrift des Regierungsrates zur Einweihung der Neubauten 18. April 1914. Zürich: Orell Füssli, n. d.

[52] ARMSTRONG, H. E.: *Nature* **120**, 1—5 (1927); KUHN, R.: *Naturwissenschaften* **36**, 1 (1949); ROBINSON, R.: Obituary Notices of Fellows of the Royal Society **22**, 609—634 (1953); FARBER, E.: In Great Chemists. Ed. by E. Farber. New York: Interscience Publishers **1961**, pp. 1365—1374; FARBER, E.: Nobel Prize Winners in Chemistry. Revised ed. New York: Abelard-Schuman **1963**, pp. 65—70.

[53] WILLSTÄTTER, R.: Aus meinem Leben: Von Arbeit, Musse und Freunden. Ed. by A. Stoll. Weinheim: Verlag Chemie **1949**; From My Life: The Memoirs of Nobel Prize Winner Richard Willstätter. Trans. by L. S. Hornig. New York: Benjamin **1965**.

[54] JAKOB, J.: Die Stereochemie der Koordinationsverbindungen. Preisschrift Universität Zürich. Zürich: Gebr. Leemann & Co. **1918**.

[55] OESPER, R. E.: *J. Chem. Educ.* **28**, 433 (1951); GÜNTHER, P.: *Z. Elektrochem.* **53**, 101—102 (1949); UNMACK, A.: *Naturhistorisk Tidende* **22**, 58—61 (1958); CHRISTIANSEN, J. A.: *Fysisk Tidsskrift* **57**, 35—36 (1959); *idem: Kemisk Maanedsblad og Nordisk Handelsblad for Kemisk Industri* **40**, 13—18 (1959); G[UGGENHEIM], E. A.: *Trans. Faraday Soc.* **55**, frontispiece (Jan., 1959); GUSTAVSON, K. H.: *J. Amer. Leath. Chemists Assoc.* **54**, 104—106 (1959); JENSEN, A. T.: *Den Kongelige Veterinaer- og Landbohøjskole Årsskrift, Nekrologer,* 91—96 (1959); *Oversigt over Det Kgl. Danske Videnskabernes Selskabs* **1958**—59, 1—15; GUGGENHEIM, E. A.: The Niels Bjerrum Memorial Lecture. *Proc. Chem. Soc.* **1960**, 104—114.

[56] BJERRUM, N.: Introductory Lecture. In Proceedings of the Symposium on Co-Ordination Chemistry, Copenhagen, August 9—13, 1953. Copenhagen: Danish Chemical Society **1954**, p. 15.

[57] BJERRUM, N.: *Kgl. Danske Videnskab. Selskab Skrifter, Naturvidenskab. math. Afdel.* [7] **4**, 1—123 (1906); *Z. physik. Chem.* **59**, 336—383, 581—604 (1907).

[58] Okáč, A.: *Chem. Listy* **40**, 197—207 (1946).

[59] HÜTTIG, G.: *Z. angew. Chem.* **40**, 41—42 (1927).

[60] KOFLER, M.: *Helv. Chim. Acta* **31**, 120—128 (1948).

[61] WALL, F. E.: *Chemist* **9**, 123—131 (1932); CAMERON, K.: *J. Amer. Chem. Soc.* **61**, 1619—1624 (1939).

[62] KARRER, P.: *Experientia* **6**, 359—360 (1950).

[63] SMILES, S.: *J. Chem. Soc.* **1948**, 396—398.

[64] STEWART, A. W.: Stereochemistry. London: Longmans, Green and Co. **1907**, 2nd ed. **1919**.

[65] — Stereochemie. Trans. by K. Löffler. Berlin: J. Springer **1908**.

[66] TILDEN, W. A.: Sir William Ramsay, Memorials of his Life and Work. London: Macmillan and Co., Ltd. **1918**; TRAVERS, M. W.: A Life of Sir William Ramsay. London: E. Arnold **1956**; MOUREU, C.: In Great Chemists. Ed. by E. Farber. New York: Interscience Publishers **1961**, pp. 997—1012.

[67] HOUBEN, J.: *Ber.* **36**, 3083 (1903).

[68] — *Ber.* **37**, 488—489 (1904).

[69] BLOMSTRAND, C. W.: Die Chemie der Jetztzeit vom Standpunkte der electrochemischen Auffassung aus Berzelius Lehre entwickelt. Heidelberg: Carl Winter's Universitäts-Buchhandlung **1869**.

[70] ROBERTSON, G. R.: *Chem. Eng. News* **25**, 3290—3291 (1947).

[71] LEWIS, G. N.: Valence and the Structure of Atoms and Molecules. New York: The Chemical Catalog Co. **1923**.

[72] RÜBEL, E.: Geschichte der Naturforschenden Gesellschaft in Zürich, 1746—1946. Zürich: Druck Gebr. Fretz **1947**.

[73] FIERZ-DAVID, H. E.: *Helv. Chim. Acta* **20**, 1335—1344 (1937).

[74] RUPE, H.: *ibid.* **27**, 1225—1252 (1944).

[75] PELET, L.: *Centenaire de la Société helvétique des Sciences naturelles, Nouveaux mémoires* **50**, 283 (1915); *Archives des Sciences physiques et naturelles* [4] **12**, 492—493 (1901); *Verhandl. Schweiz. Naturf. Ges.* **84**, 200—201 (Zofingen, 1901); *Comptes rend. Soc. helvétique des Sciences naturelles* **84**, 19—20 (Zofingen, 1901).

[76] RIVIER, H.: *Helv. Chim. Acta* **11**, 700 (1928).

[77] BRINER, E.: *J. chim. phys.* **20**, 1 (1923), trans. by E. Farber in Great Chemists. Ed. by E. Farber. New York: Interscience Publishers **1961**, pp. 1119—1127; *Helv. Chim. Acta* **5**, 411 (1922).

[78] *Verhandl. Schweiz. Naturf. Ges.* 55—57 (1918); GUYE, P. A.: *Helv. Chim. Acta* 1, 3—4 (1918); FICHTER, F.: *ibid.* 26, 3—7 (1943).

[79] Festschrift für Hans Schinz. Beiblatt zu *Vierteljahresschrift der Naturforschenden Gesellschaft in Zürich* 1928.

[80] Les Prix Nobel en 1913. Stockholm: P.-A. Norstedt & Fils, Imprimerie Royale 1914.

[81] Nobelpristragaren i kemi. *Svensk. Kemisk Tidskrift* 25, 189—192 (1913).

[82] Nobel, the Man and His Prizes. Ed. by the Nobel Foundation, 2nd rev. and enlarged ed. Amsterdam: Elsevier Publishing Co. 1962.

[83] Schweizerische Chemische Gesellschaft: Ansprachen zu Ehren des Herrn Prof. Dr. Werner gehalten bei der Versammlung vom 2. Mai 1914 in Neuenburg. Lausanne: Imprimerie Th. Eberhard 1914.

[84] LEBON, E.: Albin Haller: Biographie, Bibliographie Analytique des Écrits. Paris: Masson et Cie. 1913.

[85] *Actes Soc. helvétique des Sciences naturelles* 97, 1. Partie, 121—122 (1915).

General Bibliography (Designated in the text by G)

(1) BAILAR, J. C. (ed.): The Chemistry of the Coordination Compounds. New York: Reinhold Publ. Corp. 1956.

(2) BASOLO, F., and R. C. JOHNSON: Coordination Chemistry. New York: W. A. Benjamin, Inc. 1964.

(3) —, and R. G. PEARSON: Mechanisms of Inorganic Reactions: A Study of Metal Complexes in Solution. New York: John Wiley and Sons 1958.

(4) BERRY, A. J.: From Classical to Modern Chemistry: Some Historical Sketches. Cambridge Univ. Press 1954.

(5) — Modern Chemistry: Some Sketches of Its Historical Development. Cambridge Univ. Press 1948.

(6) BISCHOFF, C. A. (ed.): Materialien der Stereochemie in Form von Jahresberichten, 2 vols. Braunschweig: Friedrich Vieweg & Sohn 1904.

(7) CARTMELL, E., and G. W. A. FOWLES: Valency and Molecular Structure. 2nd ed. London: Butterworths 1961.

(8) COULSON, C. A.: Valence. 2nd ed. London: Oxford University Press 1961.

(9) EMELÉUS, H. J., and J. S. ANDERSON: Modern Aspects of Inorganic Chemistry. 3rd ed. Princeton, N. J.: D. Van Nostrand Co. 1960, Chaps. V—VIII.

(10) FERNELIUS, W. C.: Structure of Coordination Compounds. In Chemical Architecture. Ed. by R. E. Burk and O. Grummitt. New York: Interscience Publishers 1948, pp. 53—100.

(11) FIERZ-DAVID, H. E.: Die Entwicklungsgeschichte der Chemie. 2nd ed. Basel: Birkhäuser 1952.

(12) FREUDENBERG, K. (ed.): Stereochemie: Eine Zusammenfassung der Ergebnisse, Grundlagen und Probleme. Leipzig & Wien: Franz Deuticke 1933.

(13) Gmelins Handbuch der anorganischen Chemie. 8th ed. Weinheim/Bergstrasse: Verlag Chemie.

(14) GRADDON, D. P.: An Introduction to Co-ordination Chemistry. New York: Pergamon Press 1961.

(15) GRINBERG, A. A.: An Introduction to the Chemistry of Complex Compounds. Trans. from the 2nd Russian ed. (1951) by R. T. Leach. Ed. by D. H. Busch and R. F. Trimble. Oxford: Pergamon Press; Reading, Mass.: Addison-Wesley Publ. Co. **1962**.

(16) HENRICH, F.: Theorien der organischen Chemie. 5th ed. Braunschweig: F. Vieweg & Sohn **1924**.

(17) JONES, M. M.: Elementary Coordination Chemistry. Englewood Cliffs, N. J.: Prentice-Hall, Inc. **1964**.

(18) JØRGENSEN, C. K.: Inorganic Complexes. London—New York: Academic Press **1963**.

(19) KAUFFMANN, H.: Die Valenzlehre: Ein Lehr- und Handbuch für Chemiker und Physiker. Stuttgart: Ferdinand Enke **1911**.

(20) LADENBURG, A.: Lectures on the History of the Development of Chemistry since the Time of Lavoisier. Trans by L. Dobbin. Edinburgh: Alembic Club **1900**.

(21) LEICESTER, H. M., and H. S. KLICKSTEIN: A Source Book in Chemistry 1400—1900. Cambridge: Harvard Univ. Press **1963**.

(22) LEWIS, J., and R. G. WILKINS (ed.): Modern Coordination Chemistry. New York: Interscience Publishers, Inc. **1960**.

(23) MARTIN, D. F., and B. B. MARTIN: Coordination Compounds. New York: McGraw-Hill Book Co. **1964**.

(24) VON MEYER, E.: A History of Chemistry from Earliest Times to the Present Day. Trans. by G. McGOWAN, 3rd Engl. ed. London—New York: Macmillan and Co. **1906**.

(25) MOORE, F. J.: A History of Chemistry. 3rd ed. New York: McGraw-Hill Book Co. **1939**.

(26) MURMANN, R. K.: Inorganic Complex Compounds. New York: Reinhold Publ. Corp. **1964**.

(27) PALMER, W. G.: A History of the Concept of Valency to 1930. Cambridge Univ. Press **1965**.

(28) — Valency, Classical and Modern. Cambridge Univ. Press **1944**.

(29) PARTINGTON, J. R.: A History of Chemistry. London: Macmillan & Co.; New York: St. Martin's Press, Vol. 2, **1961**, Vol. 3, **1962**, Vol. 4, **1964**.

(30) PASCAL, P. (ed.): Nouveau Traité de Chimie Minérale. Paris: Masson et Cie.

(31) PAULING, L.: The Nature of the Chemical Bond and the Structure of Molecules and Crystals, 3rd ed. Ithaca: Cornell Univ. Press **1960**.

(32) SCHWARZ, R.: The Chemistry of the Inorganic Complex Compounds: An Introduction to Werner's Coordination Theory. Trans. by L. W. Bass. New York: J. Wiley and Sons **1923**.

(33) SIDGWICK, N. V.: The Electronic Theory of Valency. London: Oxford Univ. Press **1929**.

(34) SPEAKMAN, J. C.: An Introduction to the Modern Theory of Valency. London: E. Arnold & Co. **1935**.

(35) SYRKIN, Y. K., and M. E. DYATKINA: Structure of Molecules and the Chemical Bond. Trans. and rev. by M. A. Partridge and D. O. Jordan. New York: Dover Publications, Inc. **1964**.

(36) THOMAS, W.: Complex Salts. London: Blackie & Son **1924**.

(37) URBAIN, G., and A. SÉNÉCHAL: Introduction à la Chimie des Complexes: Théorie et Systématique de la Chimie des Complexes Minéraux. Paris: A. Hermann et Fils **1913**.

(38) WALDEN, P.: Geschichte der organischen Chemie seit 1880. Berlin: Julius Springer **1941**.

(39) WEINLAND, R.: Einführung in die Chemie der Komplex-Verbindungen (Wernersche Koordinationslehre) in elementarer Darstellung. 2nd ed. Stuttgart: Ferdinand Enke **1924**.

Biographical-Critical Bibliography   (Designated in the text by *B*)

(1) ANON.: Zum 50jährigen Bestehen der Koordinationslehre von A. Werner. *Basler Nachrichten*, Feb. 17, 1944.

(2) [BANNWARTH, E.] B., E.: Mülhauser Schlossersohn Nobelpreisträger für Chemie. *L'Alsace*, Mulhouse, p. 5 (German ed.), Nov. 10, 1963. [This article contains many errors.]

(3) B., L.: Alfred Werner. *Rev. gén. des Sciences pures et appl.* 31, 265—266 (1920).

(4) BERL, E.: Some Personal Recollections of Alfred Werner. *J. Chem. Educ.* 19, 153—154 (1942).

(5) BLOCH, E.: Alfred Werners Theorie des Kohlenstoffatoms und die Stereochemie der karbocyklischen Verbindungen. Wien und Leipzig: Kaiserl. und königl. Hof-Buchdruckerei und Hof-Verlags-Buchhandlung 1903.

(6) CHUGAEV, L. A.: Professor Alfred Werner. *Priroda, Populiarni estestvenno-istoricheskii zhurnal* 7—8, 806—832 (1914).

(7) ERNST, FRAU DR. ANNA ELISABETH: Letter to Prof. Ernst Schumacher, Aug. 20, 1963.

(8) FARBER, E.: Nobel Prize Winners in Chemistry. Rev. ed. New York: Abelard-Schuman 1963, pp. 56—60.

(9) 75 Jahre chemischer Forschung an der Universität Zürich: Festschrift zur Eröffnung des neuen Chemischen Instituts, verfasst von den Studierenden der Chemie, n. d. [Zürich 1909], pp. 60—84.

(10) 25 Nobel Preisträger: ihre wissenschaftliche Leistung und ihre Veröffentlichungen. Braunschweig: F. Vieweg & Sohn, n. d. [prob. 1955].

(11) [GORDON, N. E.]: *J. Chem. Educ.* 7, 1733—1735 (1930).

(12) HUBER, R.: Alfred Werner. *Schweizerische Chemiker Zeitung* 7, 73—80 (1920).

(13) HUBER, DR. ROBERT: Letter to Prof. Ernst Schumacher, Aug. 8, 1960.

(14) — Letter to Prof. Ernst Schumacher, Oct. 15, 1960.

(15) — Letter to Frau Dr. Anna Elisabeth Ernst, Mar. 10, 1960.

(16) KARRER, P.: Prof. Alfred Werner †. (a) *Neue Zürcher Zeitung*, Nr. 1804, Erstes Morgenblatt, p. 1 Feuilleton, Nov. 21, 1919; (b) reprinted in *Vierteljahresschrift der Naturforschenden Gesellschaft in Zürich* 64, 851—854 (1919).

(17) — Alfred Werner. *Helv. Chim. Acta* 3, 196—232, 432 (1920).

(18) — Alfred Werner 1866—1919. Nekrologe und Biographien verstorbener Mitglieder der Schweizerischen Naturforschenden Gesellschaft und Verzeichnisse ihrer Publikationen. In *Verhandlungen der Schweizerischen Naturforschenden Gesellschaft*, Neuchâtel 1920, pp. 45—53.

(19) — Entstehung und Entwicklung der Koordinationslehre von Alfred Werner. *Vierteljahresschrift der Naturforschenden Gesellschaft in Zürich* 89, 1—16 (1944); *Schweiz. Chem.-Ztg. u. Tech. Ind.* 27, 93—94 (1944).

(20) KING, V. L.: A Rought but Brilliant Diamond. *J. Chem. Educ.* 19, 345 (1942).

(21) KLEMM, W.: Zum 75. Geburtstage Alfred Werners. *Z. anorg. allgem. Chem.* 248, 314—318 (1941).

(22) LIFSCHITZ, I.: Alfred Werner †. *Z. Elektrochem.* 26, 514—529 (1920); see also KOETS, P.: *ibid.* 28, 324 (1922).

(23) MORGAN, G. T.: Alfred Werner. *J. Chem. Soc.* 117, 1639—1648 (1920).

(24) PFEIFFER, P.: "Vorwort" to reference A 14 (a).

(25) — Die diesjährigen Träger der Nobelpreise für Chemie und Physik: Alfred Werner. *Chemiker-Zeitung* **148**, 1517—1518 (1913).

(26) — Alfred Werner. *Z. angew. Chem.* **33**, 37—39 (1920).

(27) — Alfred Werner. *Ber.* **53** A, 9—10 (1920).

(28) — Prof. Dr. Alfred Werner. In Rektoratsrede und Jahresbericht der Universität Zürich, April 1919 bis Ende März 1920. Zürich: Orell Füssli **1919/1920**, pp. 51—53.

(29) — Alfred Werner. Deutsches Biographisches Jahrbuch, 1917—1920. Stuttgart, **1928**, Vol. 2, pp. 484—489.

(30) — Alfred Werner. *J. Chem. Educ.* **5**, 1090—1098 (1928).

(31) — Alfred Werner. In Great Chemists. Ed. by E. Farber. New York: Interscience Publishers **1961**, pp. 1233—1243.

(32) READ, J.: Humour and Humanism in Chemistry. London: G. Bell and Sons **1947**, pp. 262—284.

(33) Rektorats-Archiv, Universität Zürich Aktenverzeichnis, Mappe Nr. 140 A/7, Dozenten, Persönliches, Alfred Werner.

(34) REITZENSTEIN, F.: Über die verschiedenen Theorien zur Erklärung der Konstitution der Metallammoniaksalzen. *Z. anorg. Chem.* **18**, 152—210 (1898).

(35) SCHLEICH, K.: Alfred Werner (12. Dez. 1866 — 15. Nov. 1919). *Neue Zürcher Nachrichten*, Feuilleton, Nov. 20, 1919.

(36) SCHWARZ, H.: La théorie de coordination de M. A. Werner et son importance pour la chimie minérale. *Le Moniteur Scientifique-Quesneville* [4] **23**, 289—297 (1909).

(37) Schweizerische Chemische Gesellschaft: Ansprachen zu Ehren des Herrn Prof. Dr. Werner gehalten bei der Versammlung vom 2. Mai 1914 in Neuenburg. Lausanne: Imprimerie Th. Eberhard [1914].

(38) SKANAVI-GRIGOR'EVA, M. S.: Alfred Werner (Po lichnym vospaminaniiam avtora). *Uspekhi Khimii* **14**, 333—337 (1945).

(39) *Staatsarchiv Zürich*, U 110 b, Fasc. 34.

(40) STAUDINGER, H.: Die drei Nobelpreisträger, Adolf von Baeyer, Emil Fischer und Alfred Werner. *Vierteljahresschrift der Naturforschenden Gesellschaft in Zürich* **65**, Sitzungsberichte, III—V (1920).

(41) UEMURA, T.: *Kagaku* (Kyoto) **16**, 189—193 (1961).

(42) VETTER, T.: Trauerrede, Nov. 17, 1919, 5 pp. typed.

Bibliography of the Works of Alfred Werner

Articles (Designated in the text by *A*)

1890 (1) (With A. Hantzsch) "Über räumliche Anordnung der Atome in stickstoffhaltigen Molekülen," *Ber.* **23**, 11—30; (a) "Foundation of nitrogen stereochemistry: Alfred Werner's Inaugural Dissertation" (translated with commentary by G. B. Kauffman), *J. Chem. Educ.* **43**, 155—165 (1966).

  (2) (With A. Hantzsch) "Bemerkungen über stereochemisch isomere Stickstoffverbindungen," *Ber.* **23**, 1243—1253.

  (3) "Über ein zweites Benzoïnoxim," *Ber.* **23**, 2333—2336.

(4) "Über zwei stereochemisch isomere Derivate des Furfuraldoxims," *Ber.* **23**, 2336—2339.

(5) (With A. Hantzsch) "Bemerkungen über stereochemisch isomere Stickstoffverbindungen," *Ber.* **23**, 2764—2769.

(6) "Über räumliche Anordnung der Atome in stickstoffhaltigen Molekülen," Dissertation, Universität Zürich, Druck von A. Diggelmann, Uster-Zürich.

1891 (7) "Beiträge zur Theorie der Affinität und Valenz," *Vierteljahrsschrift der Zürcher Naturforschenden Gesellschaft* **36**, 129—169; (a) "Alfred Werner's Habilitationsschrift 'Contributions to the Theory of Affinity and Valence'" (translated with commentary by G. B. Kauffman), *Chymia* **12** (1966) (in press).

(8) "Beiträge zur Theorie der Affinität und Valenz," Habilitationsschrift, Eidgenössisches Polytechnikum, Zürich.

1892 (9) "Sur un nitrate basique de calcium," *Ann. chim. et phys.* [6] **27**, 570—574; *Compt. rend.* **115**, 169—171.

(10) "Über Stereoisomerie bei Derivaten der Benzhydroxamsäure." [I.], *Ber.* **25**, 27—48.

1893 (11) "Über Stereoisomerie bei Derivaten der Benzhydroxamsäure." [II.], *Ber.* **26**, 1562—1567.

(12) "Über Hydroxylaminessigsäure und Derivate derselben," *Ber.* **26**, 1567—1571.

(13) (With A. Hantzsch) "Entgegnung" [Reply to W. Lossen], *Ber.* **26**, 2069—2070.

(14) "Beitrag zur Konstitution anorganischer Verbindungen." [I.], *Z. anorg. Chem.* **3**, 267—330; (a) Ostwald's Klassiker der exakten Wissenschaften Nr. 212 (edited by P. Pfeiffer), Akademische Verlagsgesellschaft M. B. H., Leipzig **1924**; (1) Review: *Z. Elektrochem.* **31**, 517—518 (1925); (b) "Contribution to the Constitution of Inorganic Compounds," in "Classics in Coordination Chemistry: Part I: The Selected Papers of Alfred Werner (1866—1919)" (translated, edited, and with commentary by G. B. Kauffman), Dover Publications, Inc., New York (in press).

(15) (With A. Miolati) "Beiträge zur Konstitution anorganischer Verbindungen. I.," *Z. physik. Chem.* **12**, 35—55; (a) "Contributo allo studio della costituzione dei composti inorganici" [I.], *Gazz. chim. ital.* **23** II, 140—165; (b) "Contributions to the Constitution of Inorganic Compounds. First Article," in "Classics in Coordination Chemistry: Part I" (translated, edited, and with commentary by G. B. Kauffman), Dover Publications, Inc., New York (in press).

1894 (16) (With A. Miolati) "Beiträge zur Konstitution anorganischer Verbindungen. II.," *Z. physik. Chem.* **14**, 506—521; (a) "Contributo allo studio della costituzione dei composti inorganici. II.," *Gazz. chim. ital.* **24** II, 408—427; (b) "Contributions to the Constitution of Inorganic Compounds. Second Article," in "Classics in Coordination Chemistry: Part I" (translated, edited, and with commentary by G. B. Kauffman), Dover Publications, Inc., New York (in press).

(17) "Über Dinitrophenyläther von Oximen," *Ber.* **27**, 1654—1657.

(18) (With H. Buss) "Über Benzhydroximsäurechlorid," *Ber.* **27**, 2193—2201.

(19) "Über Hydroximsäurechloride und ihre Umwandlungsprodukte," *Ber.* **27**, 2846—2850.

(20) (With E. Sonnenfeld) "Über Hydroxylaminessigsäure und α-Hydroxylaminpropionsäure," *Ber.* **27**, 3350—3354.

1895 (21) "Beitrag zur Konstitution anorganischer Verbindungen. II.," *Z. anorg. Chem.* **8**, 153—188.

(22) "Beitrag zur Konstitution anorganischer Verbindungen. III. Über Beziehungen zwischen Koordinations- und Valenzverbindungen," *Z. anorg. Chem.* **8**, 189—197.

(23) (With H. Buss) "Beobachtungen über Benzyläther von Oximen," *Ber.* 28, 1278—1280.

(24) (With H. Buss) "Beobachtungen über Nitrolsäuren," *Ber.* 28, 1280—1282.

(25) (With F. Bial) "Über Hydroxylaminisobuttersäure," *Ber.* 28, 1374—1379.

(26) (With A. Klein) "Über sogenannte amidochromsaure Salze," *Z. anorg. Chem.* 9, 291—294.

(27) "Beitrag zur Konstitution anorganischer Verbindungen. IV.," *Z. anorg. Chem.* 9, 382—417.

1896 (28) "Über eine eigentümliche Klasse von Platinverbindungen und die sogenannten isomeren Platosoxalsäuren," *Z. anorg. Chem.* 12, 46—54.

(29) "Über Chlorosalze," *Vierteljahrsschrift der Zürcher Naturforschenden Gesellschaft* 41, 254—269.

(30) "Über Stereoisomerie bei Derivaten der Benzhydroxamsäure. III.," *Ber.* 29, 1146—1153.

(31) (With J. Subak) "Über Stereoisomerie bei Derivaten der Benzhydroxamsäure. IV.," *Ber.* 29, 1153—1161.

(32) (With A. Gemeseus) "Über Aethylendihydroxylamin," *Ber.* 29, 1161—1164.

(33) (With R. Falck) "Über α-Hydroxylaminbuttersäure," *Ber.* 29, 2654—2659.

(34) "Über die Benzylirung des Acetaldoxims," *Ber.* 29, 2667.

(35) (With A. Miolati) "Beiträge zur Konstitution anorganischer Verbindungen. III.," *Z. physik. Chem.* 21, 225—238; (a) "Contributo allo studio della costituzione dei composti inorganici. III.," *Gazz. chim. ital.* 27, 299—316.

1897 (36) "Beitrag zur Konstitution anorganischer Verbindungen. V. Die Kobaltammoniak- verbindungen und ihre Nomenklatur," *Z. anorg. Chem.* 14, 21—27.

(37) (With A. Klein) "Beitrag zur Konstitution anorganischer Verbindungen. VI. Über 1.6-Dichlorotetramminkobaltisalze (Chloropraseosalze)," *Z. anorg. Chem.* 14, 28—41.

(38) (With P. Ferchland, W. Schmujlow, A. Maiborn, and M. Stephani) "Beitrag zur Konstitution anorganischer Verbindungen. VII. Über die Molekulargrösse anorga- nischer Salze," *Z. anorg. Chem.* 15, 1—41.

(39) (With F. Fassbender) "Beitrag zur Konstitution anorganischer Verbindungen. VIII. Über die *Anderson*'sche Reaktion," *Z. anorg. Chem.* 15, 123—142.

(40) "Beitrag zur Konstitution anorganischer Verbindungen. IX. Über Triammin- und Diamminkobaltisalze," *Z. anorg. Chem.* 15, 143—172.

(41) (With G. Richter) "Beitrag zur Konstitution anorganischer Verbindungen. X. Über ammoniakalische Chromsulfocyanverbindungen und Stereoisomerie bei denselben," *Z. anorg. Chem.* 15, 243—277.

1898 (42) (With F. Beddow, A. Baselli, and F. Steinitzer) "Beitrag zur Konstitution anorgani- scher Verbindungen. XI. Über komplexe Kobaltammoniakverbindungen," *Z. anorg. Chem.* 16, 109—166.

(43) (With A. Mylius) "Beitrag zur Konstitution anorganischer Verbindungen. XII. Über Oxykobaltiake und Anhydrooxykobaltiake," *Z. anorg. Chem.* 16, 245—267.

(44) (With H. Grüger) "Beitrag zur Konstitution anorganischer Verbindungen. XIII. Über Sulfitokobaltamminverbindungen," *Z. anorg. Chem.* 16, 398—423.

(45) (With P. Pfeiffer) "Beitrag zur Konstitution anorganischer Verbindungen. XIV. Über Molekülverbindungen der Zinntetrahalogenide und der Zinnalkyle," *Z. anorg. Chem.* 17, 82—110.

1899 (46) "Beitrag zur Konstitution anorganischer Verbindungen. XV. Über Chlorosalze," *Z. anorg. Chem.* **19**, 158—178.

(47) (With F. Steinitzer and K. Rücker) "Beitrag zur Konstitution anorganischer Verbindungen. XVI. Über komplexe Kobaltammoniakverbindungen," *Z. anorg. Chem.* **21**, 96—115.

(48) (With A. Vilmos) "Beitrag zur Konstitution anorganischer Verbindungen. XVII. Über Oxalatodiäthylendiaminkobaltisalze $\left(Co \, {C_2 O_4 \atop en_2}\right) X$," *Z. anorg. Chem.* **21**, 145—158.

(49) (With W. Spruck, W. Megerle, and J. Pastor) "Beitrag zur Konstitution anorganischer Verbindungen. XVIII. Über Äthylendiamin- und Propylendiaminverbindungen von Salzen zweiwertiger Metalle," *Z. anorg. Chem.* **21**, 201—242.

(50) (With E. Grebe) "Beitrag zur Konstitution anorganischer Verbindungen. XIX. Über Platinoxalatoverbindungen," *Z. anorg. Chem.* **21**, 377—388.

(51) (With H. Müller, R. Klien, and F. Bräunlich) "Beitrag zur Konstitution anorganischer Verbindungen. XX. Über rhodanatokobaltiake [*sic*] und strukturisomere Salze," *Z. anorg. Chem.* **22**, 91—157.

(52) (With W. Skiba) "Über Umlagerungen in der Benzhydroximsäuregruppe," *Ber.* **32**, 1654—1666.

(53) (With C. Bloch) "Über Chlorbenzhydroximsäurechlorid und Umwandlungsproducte desselben," *Ber.* **32**, 1975—1985.

(54) (With T. Herberger) "Über Ringschlüsse unter Abspaltung aromatisch gebundener Nitrogruppen," *Ber.* **32**, 2686—2696.

(55) (With H. E. Conrad) "Über die optisch aktiven Transhexahydrophtalsäuren," *Ber.* **32**, 3046—3055.

(56) (With E. Stiasny) "Über Nitroderivate des Azo-, Azoxy- und Hydrazo-Benzols," *Ber.* **32**, 3256—3282.

1901 (57) (With A. Gubser) "Zur Kenntniss der Verbindungen des Chroms. I. Über die Hydrate des Chromchlorids," *Ber.* **34**, 1579—1604.

(58) "Über Isomerien bei anorganischen Verbindungen. I. Über stereoisomere Kobaltverbindungen," *Ber.* **34**, 1705—1719.

(59) (With E. Humphrey) "Über Isomerien bei anorganischen Verbindungen. II. Über stereoisomere Dinitrodiaethylendiaminkobaltsalze $\left(Co \, {(NO_2)_2 \atop en_2}\right) X$," *Ber.* **34**, 1719—1732.

(60) "Über Isomerien bei anorganischen Verbindungen. III. Über 1.6-Chloronitrito-diäthylendiaminkobaltsalze," *Ber.* **34**, 1733—1738.

(61) (With L. Gerb) "Über Isomerien bei anorganischen Verbindungen. IV. Über 1.2-Chloronitritodiäthylendiaminkobaltiverbindungen," *Ber.* **34**, 1739—1745.

(62) (With J. Kunz) "Über Phenanthrylamine [Vorläufige Mittheilung]," *Ber.* **34**, 2524—2528.

(63) "Über Acetylacetonverbindungen des Platins," *Ber.* **34**, 2584—2593.

(64) (With K. Dinklage) "Über Nitrilopentachloroösmiumsaure Salze und die Constitution der Osmiamsäure," *Ber.* **34**, 2698—2703.

(65) "Über Carboxonium- und Carbothionium-Salze [Vorläufige Mittheilung]," *Ber.* **34**, 3300—3311.

(66) (With C. Herty) "Beiträge zur Konstitution anorganischer Verbindungen. IV.," *Z. physik. Chem.* **38**, 331—352.

1902 (67) (With J. Klien) "Über Tetraquodiammin- und Diacidodiaquodiammin-Chromsalze," *Ber.* **35**, 277—291.

(68) (With J. Kunz) "Über Oxyphenanthrencarbonsäuren," *Ber.* **35**, 4419—4429.

(69) (With B. Löwenstein, A. Wack, T. Frey, M. Kunz, K. Rekner, A. Ney, H. Heil, A. Scherrer, H. Schwabacher, J. Kunz, and A. Grob) "Beitrag zur Chemie des Phenanthrens," *Ann.* **321**, 248—357; **322**, 135—173.

(70) "Über Haupt- und Nebenvalenzen und die Constitution der Ammoniumverbindungen," *Ann.* **322**, 261—296.

(71) (With Dr. Kalkmann and A. Gubser) "Über die Constitution der Oxoniumsalze," *Ann.* **322**, 296—351.

1903 (72) "Die Ammoniumsalze als einfachste Metallammoniake," *Ber.* **36**, 147—159.

(73) (With F. Zilkens) "Über eine neue Synthese von Kohlenwasserstoffen [Vorläufige Mittheilung]," *Ber.* **36**, 2116—2118.

(74) (With N. Goslings) "Über Carbonatopentamminkobaltsalze," *Ber.* **36**, 2378—2382.

(75) "Eine neue Synthese von Kohlenwasserstoffen mittels magnesiumorganischer Verbindungen," *Ber.* **36**, 3618—3619.

1904 (76) (With A. Grob) "9.10-Diphenyl-phenanthren, ein Product intramolekularer Umlagerungen," *Ber.* **37**, 2887—2903.

(77) (With A. Egger) "Zur Kenntniss des sogenannten β-Dibromphenanthrens," *Ber.* **37**, 3026—3030.

(78) "Untersuchungen in der Phenanthrenreihe. Antwort an Hrn. Julius Schmidt," *Ber.* **37**, 3083—3088.

(79) (With W. Seybold) "Zur Kenntniss einer neuen Esterificirungsmethode für organische Säuren," *Ber.* **37**, 3658—3661.

(80) (With A. Piguet) "*Beckmann*'sche Umlagerung durch Benzolsulfonsäurechlorid bei Gegenwart von Alkali oder Pyridin," *Ber.* **37**, 4295—4315.

(81) (With A. Grün) "Über Triamminkobaltsalze und einen neuen Fall von Hydratisomerie," *Ber.* **37**, 4700—4706.

(82) (With O. Meister) "Prof. Dr. Viktor Merz. 1839—1904," *Verhandlungen der Schweizerischen Naturforschenden Gesellschaft*, Winterthur, **1904**, Nekrolog, pp. LX—CIII.

1905 (83) (With T. Detscheff) "Die *Beckmann*'sche Umlagerung bei Oximen benzoïnartig constituirter Ketonalkohole," *Ber.* **38**, 69—84.

(84) (With E. Berl) "Zur Kenntniss der Hexahydroxylamin-kobaltisalze," *Ber.* **38**, 893—899.

(85) "Beitrag zum Ausbau des periodischen Systems," *Ber.* **38**, 914—921.

(86) (With R. Feenstra) "Über eine Grenzreihe der Dikobaltiake," *Ber.* **38**, 923—925.

(87) (With A. Wolberg) "Über Dibromo-tetrammin-kobaltsalze," *Ber.* **38**, 992—998.

(88) (With A. Wolberg) "Zur Kenntniss der Bromo-aquo-tetrammin-kobaltsalze," *Ber.* **38**, 2009—2013.

(89) "Zur periodischen Anordnung der Elemente," *Ber.* **38**, 2022—2027.

(90) (With A. Grün) "Über gemischte Aethylendiamin und Ammoniak enthaltende Triamminkobaltsalze," *Ber.* **38**, 4033—4040.

1906 (91) (With P. Schorndorff and C. Chorower) "Über den Einfluss von Alkoxygruppen auf die Reactionsfähigkeit α-ständiger Bromatome in aromatischen Verbindungen," *Ber.* **39**, 27—36.

(92) (With W. Peters) "Über die Condensation von Phenylhydrazin mit *p*-Chlor-*m*-nitro-benzoësäureester," *Ber.* **39**, 185—192.

(93) (With R. Huber) "Zur Kenntniss der Verbindungen des Chroms. III. Untersuchungen über Chromsalze," *Ber.* **39**, 329—338.

(94) (With K. Dinklage) "Über Nitrilo-bromo-osmonate," *Ber.* **39**, 499—503.

(95) (With P. Gerhardt, G. Schöler, W. Zipser, A. Summerer, and [T.] Huesmann) "Über den wechselnden Affinitätswerth einfacher Bindungen," *Ber.* **39**, 1278—1292.

(96) (With R. Feenstra) "Über Dichlorotetrapyridinkobaltsalze," *Ber.* **39**, 1538—1545.

(97) (With A. Gubser) "Zur Kenntniss der Verbindungen des Chroms. IV. Über die Hydrate des Chromchlorids," *Ber.* **39**, 1823—1830.

(98) "Zur Kenntniss der Verbindungen des Chroms. V. Über Triamminchromisalze, ein Beitrag zur Chemie der Hydrate," *Ber.* **39**, 2656—2667.

(99) (With J. v. Halban) "Zur Kenntniss der Chromsalze [*sic*]. VI. Über Rhodanatochrom-ammoniaksalze," *Ber.* **39**, 2668—2673.

(100) (With E. Bindschedler) "Über Trichloro-triammin-kobalt und seine Hydrate," *Ber.* **39**, 2673—2679.

(101) (With F. Bräunlich, E. Rogowina, and C. Kreutzer) "Über raumisomere Hexammin-salze," in "Festschrift Adolf Lieben zum fünfzigjährigen Doktorjubiläum und zum siebzigsten Geburtstage von Freunden, Verehrern und Schülern gewidmet," C. F. Winter'sche Verlagsbuchhandlung, Leipzig **1906**, pp. 197—218; (a) *Ann.* **351**, 65—86 (1907).

1907 (102) (With G. Jantsch) "Über stereoismere Diaquo-diäthylendiaminkobaltisalze. [(H$_2$O)$_2$Coen$_2$]X$_3$," *Ber.* **40**, 262—271.

(103) "Zur Theorie der Hydrolyse und über stereoisomere Hydroxo-aquo-diäthylen-diamin-kobaltsalze. [I.]," *Ber.* **40**, 272—287.

(104) "Zur Theorie der Hydrolyse. II. Über Hydroxo-aquo-dipyridin-diammin- und Diaquo-dipyridin-diammin-Kobaltsalze," *Ber.* **40**, 468—479.

(105) (With E. Zinggeler) "Über strukturisomere Salze der Rhodanwasserstoffsäure und der salpetrigen Säure," *Ber.* **40**, 765—788.

(106) (With K. Dawe) "Über Diisorhodanato-dipropylendiamin- und Dipropylendiamin-diammin-kobaltisalze," *Ber.* **40**, 789—799.

(107) (With E. Berl, E. Zinggeler, and G. Jantsch) "Über mehrkernige Metallammoniake. III. Über Dodekammin-hexoltetrakobaltsalze und Hexaäthylendiamin-hexoltetra-kobaltisalze: $\left\{ Co \left[\begin{smallmatrix} HO \\ HO \end{smallmatrix} CoA_4 \right]_3 \right\} X_6$," *Ber.* **40**, 2103—2125.

(108) (With A. Fröhlich) "Über stereoisomere Dichloro-dipropylendiamin-kobaltsalze," *Ber.* **40**, 2225—2235.

(109) "Zur Theorie der Hydrolyse. III. Zur Kenntnis der Rutheniumammoniakverbin-dungen," *Ber.* **40**, 2614—2628.

(110) (With J. Jovanovits) "Über eine Reihe von komplexen Acetatochromverbindungen," *Schweizerische Wissenschaftliche Nachrichten* 1 B, 1—7.

(111) (With J. Dubsky) "Zur Theorie der Hydrolyse. IV. Über Dihydroxo-diaquo-diammin-chromisalze, $\left[\begin{smallmatrix} HO \\ HO \end{smallmatrix} Cr \begin{smallmatrix} (OH_2)_2 \\ (NH_3)_2 \end{smallmatrix} \right] X$, *Ber.* **40**, 4085—4093.

(112) "Zur Theorie der Hydrolyse. V. Über Dihydroxo-tetrammin-platinverbindungen," *Ber.* **40**, 4093—4097.

(113) "Zur Theorie der Hydrolyse. VI. Über Hydroxo-pentammin-kobaltisalze," *Ber.* **40**, 4098—4112.

(114) "Über Hydroxo-aquo-tetrammin-kobaltisalze," *Ber.* **40**, 4113—4117.

(115) "Über Hydroxo-nitro-tetrammin-kobaltisalze," *Ber.* **40**, 4117—4122.

(116) "Über anomale anorganische Oxoniumsalze, eine neue Klasse basischer Salze," *Ber.* **40**, 4122—4128.

(117) "Über Chloro-nitro-tetrammin-kobaltisalze," *Ber.* **40**, 4128—4132.

(118) "Zur Theorie der Basen," *Ber.* **40**, 4133—4145.

(119) (With G. Jantsch) "Über mehrkernige Metallammoniake. IV. Über Tetraäthylen-diamin-diaquo-tetrolkobaltodikobaltisalze, $\left[Co^{II} {(OH_2)_2 \atop ((HO)_2} Co^{III} en_2)_2 \right] X_4$," *Ber.* **40**, 4426—4434.

(120) "Über mehrkernige Metallammoniake. V. Über Octammin-dioldikobaltisalze," *Ber.* **40**, 4434—4441.

(121) "Zur Konstitution basischer Salze und analog konstituierter Komplexsalze. I.," *Ber.* **40**, 4441—4449.

(122) "Über mehrkernige Metallammoniake. VI. Über Octammin-μ-amino-ol-dikobalti-salze. $\left[(H_3N)_4 Co {\cdot NH_2 \cdot \atop \cdot OH \cdot} Co (NH_3)_4 \right] X_4$," *Ber.* **40**, 4605—4615.

(123) "Über 1.2-Dichloro-tetrammin-kobaltisalze (Ammoniak-violeosalze)," *Ber.* **40**, 4817—4825; (a) "On 1.2-Dichloro-tetrammine-cobalti Salts (Ammonia-violeo Salts)," in "Classics in Coordination Chemistry: Part I" (translated, edited, and with commentary by G. B. Kauffman), Dover Publications, Inc., New York (in press).

(124) (With E. Bindschedler and A. Grün) "Über mehrkernige Metallammoniake. VII. Über Hexammin-triol-dikobaltisalze, $\left[(H_3N)_3 Co {\cdot OH \cdot \atop \cdot OH \cdot \atop \cdot OH \cdot} Co (NH_3)_3 \right] X_3$," *Ber.* **40**, 4834—4844.

1908 (125) (With E. Thomann) "Zur Theorie der Beizenfarbstoffe" [I.], *Ber.* **41**, 1062—1071.

(126) "Zur Theorie der Beizenfarbstoffe" [II.], *Ber.* **41**, 2383—2386.

(127) "Über Jodopentamminkobaltisalze, $\left[Co {J \atop (NH_3)_5} \right] X_2$," *Ber.* **41**, 3007—3015.

(128) (With J. Jovanovits, G. Aschkinasy, and J. Posselt) "Zur Kenntnis der organischen Metallsalze. I. Über ameisensaure und essigsaure Salze des Chroms," *Ber.* **41**, 3447—3465.

(129) "Über mehrkernige Metallammoniake. VIII. Über die Umwandlung von Hexammin-triol-dikobaltisalzen in Octammin-diol-dikobaltisalze," *Ber.* **41**, 3879—3884.

(130) "Über mehrkernige Metallammoniake. IX. Über Dekammin-μ-amino-dikobaltisalze," *Ber.* **41**, 3912—3921.

(131) (With N. Costachescu) "Zur Kenntnis der Verbindungen des Chroms. VII. Über die Hydrate des Chromfluorids und einen Fall von Koordinationspolymerie bei Hydraten," *Ber.* **41**, 4242—4246.

1909 (132) "Über die wissenschaftliche Tätigkeit von Prof. Dr. Viktor Merz in Zürich," in Diergart, Paul (ed.), "Beiträge aus der Geschichte der Chemie dem Gedächtnis von Georg W. A. Kahlbaum," Franz Deuticke, Leipzig und Wien 1909, pp. 621—631.

(133) (With O. de Vries) "Über complexe Iridiumverbindungen," *Ann.* **364**, 77—127.

(134) "Zur Frage nach den Beziehungen zwischen Farbe und Konstitution [Vorläufige Mitteilung]," *Ber.* **42**, 4324—4328.

(135) "Les bases théoriques des formules de structure des composés inorganiques," *Archives des Sciences physiques et naturelles* [4] **28**, 317—332.

1910 (*136*) (With F. Salzer, M. Pieper, J. Fürstenberg, S. Malmgren, M. Grigorieff, A. Grün, E. Bindschedler, and E. Welti) "Über mehrkernige Metallammoniake. X.," *Ann.* **375**, 1—144.

(*137*) "Zur Kenntnis der Verbindungen des Chroms. VIII. Über Triammin-chromsalze," *Ber.* **43**, 2286—2295.

1911 (*138*) "Über den räumlichen Stellungswechsel bei Umsetzungen von raumisomeren Verbindungen," *Ber.* **44**, 873—882.

(*139*) (With V. L. King) "Zur Kenntnis des asymmetrischen Kobaltatoms. I.," *Ber.* **44**, 1887—1898; (a) "Toward an Understanding of the Asymmetric Cobalt Atom. I.," in "Classics in Coordination Chemistry: Part I" (translated, edited, and with commentary by G. B. Kauffman), Dover Publications, Inc., New York (in press).

(*140*) "Zur Kenntnis des asymmetrischen Kobaltatoms. II.," *Ber.* **44**, 2445—2455.

(*141*) "Über Spiegelbildisomerie bei Chromverbindungen. I.," *Ber.* **44**, 3132—3140.

(*142*) "Zur Kenntnis des asymmetrischen Kobaltatoms. III.," *Ber.* **44**, 3272—3278.

(*143*) "Zur Kenntnis des asymmetrischen Kobaltatoms. IV.," *Ber.* **44**, 3279—3284.

(*144*) "Les composés optiquement actifs du cobalt et du chrome," *Archives des Sciences physiques et naturelles* [4] **32**, 457—467.

1912 (*145*) (With J. Rapiport, R. Hartmuth, M. Pokrowska, K. R. Lange, R. Bosshard, L. Gerb, S. Lorie, E. Schmidt, W. E. Boës, C. Rix, R. Samanek, N. Goslings, F. Chaussy, and G. Lindenberg) "Über die raumisomeren Kobaltverbindungen," *Ann.* **386**, 1—272.

(*146*) "Zur Kenntnis des asymmetrischen Kobaltatoms. V.," *Ber.* **45**, 121—130.

(*147*) "Über Spiegelbild-Isomerie bei Eisenverbindungen (Vorläufige Mitteilung)," *Ber.* **45**, 433—436.

(*148*) "Über neue spiegelbildisomere Metallverbindungen," *Chemiker-Zeitung* **44**, 401.

(*149*) "Über Spiegelbildisomerie bei Chromverbindungen. II.," *Ber.* **45**, 865—869.

(*150*) "Über Spiegelbildisomerie bei Rhodium-Verbindungen. I.," *Ber.* **45**, 1228—1236.

(*151*) "Über Spiegelbild-Isomerie bei Chromverbindungen. III.," *Ber.* **45**, 3061—3070.

(*152*) (With [T. P.] McCutcheon) "Zur Kenntnis des asymmetrischen Kobaltatoms. VI.," *Ber.* **45**, 3281—3287.

(*153*) (With Y. Shibata) "Zur Kenntnis des asymmetrischen Kobaltatoms. VII.," *Ber.* **45**, 3287—3293.

(*154*) (With G. Tschernoff) "Zur Kenntnis des asymmetrischen Kobaltatoms. VIII.," *Ber.* **45**, 3294—3301.

1913 (*155*) (With M. Basyrin) "Über die optisch aktiven Dimethyl-bernsteinsäuren," *Ber.* **46**, 3229—3232.

(*156*) "Valenzlehre," in "Handwörterbuch der Naturwissenschaften," Zehnter Band, Verlag von Gustav Fischer, Jena **1913**, pp. 165—180.

(*157*) "Zur Kenntnis des asymmetrischen Kobaltatoms. IX.," *Ber.* **46**, 3674—3683.

1914 (*158*) (With E. Bindschedler, E. Blatter, C. Sackur, H. Schwarz, and H. Surber) "Über Metallverbindungen mit komplex gebundener Oxalsäure. I. Über Monooxaloverbindungen," *Ann.* **405**, 212—241.

(*159*) (With W. J. Bowis, A. Hoblik, H. Schwarz, and H. Surber) "Über Metallverbindungen mit komplex gebundener Oxalsäure. II. Über Dioxaloverbindungen," *Ann.* **406**, 261—331.

(160) "Über die asymmetrisch gebauten chemischen Moleküle," in "Universität Zürich, Festgabe zur Einweihung der Neubauten, 18. April 1914," Schulthess & Co., Zürich **1914**, pp. 65—79.

(161) (With J. Poupardin) "Über Spiegelbild-Isomerie bei Rhodium-Verbindungen. II.," *Ber.* **47**, 1954—1960.

(162) (With H. Kuh and P. Wüst) "Zur Kenntnis des asymmetrischen Kobaltatoms. X.," *Ber.* **47**, 1961—1979.

(163) (With J. Bosshart) "Zur Kenntnis des asymmetrischen Kobaltatoms. XI. Über Oxalo-diäthylendiamin-kobaltisalze und eine neue Spaltungsmethode für racemische anorganische Verbindungen," *Ber.* **47**, 2171—2182.

(164) "Zur Kenntnis des asymmetrischen Kobaltatoms. XII., Über optische Aktivität bei kohlenstofffreien Verbindungen," *Ber.* **47**, 3087—3094; (a) "Toward an Understanding of the Asymmetric Cobalt Atom. XII. On Optical Activity among Carbon-Free Compounds," in "Classics in Coordination Chemistry: Part I" (translated, edited, and with commentary by G. B. Kauffman), Dover Publications, Inc., New York (in press).

(165) "S. M. Jörgensen †. 4. Juli 1837—1. April 1914," *Chemiker-Zeitung* **38**, 557—564.

1916 (166) (With J. A. Siemssen) "Über Trirhodanato-aquo-diammin-chrom," *Ber.* **49**, 1539—1544.

(167) "Über die Koordinationszahl 'acht' und über die wechselnde Koordinationszahl," June, 1916 (typewritten manuscript); (a) "A Recently Discovered Manuscript by Alfred Werner, 'On Coordination Number Eight and the Variable Coordination Number'" (translated with commentary by G. B. Kauffman), *Chymia* **12** (in press).

1917 (168) "Über Spiegelbildisomerie bei Platinverbindungen. I.," *Vierteljahrsschrift der Naturforschenden Gesellschaft in Zürich* **62**, 553—564.

1918 (169) "Über eine neue Isomerieart bei Kobaltverbindungen und Verbindungen mit asymmetrischem Kobalt und Kohlenstoff," *Helv. Chim. Acta* **1**, 5—32.

(170) (With P. Karrer) "Über Nitroso-pentamminkobaltisalze," *Helv. Chim. Acta* **1**, 54—78.

(171) (With S. Matissen) "Zur Konstitution der inneren Metallkomplexsalze," *Helv. Chim. Acta* **1**, 78—84.

1920 (172) (With A. P. Smirnoff) "Über optisch-aktive Iridiumverbindungen," *Helv. Chim. Acta* **3**, 472—486.

(173) (With A. P. Smirnoff) "Zur Stereochemie des Rutheniumatoms," *Helv. Chim. Acta* **3**, 737—747.

1921 (174) (With J. E. Schwyzer and W. Karrer) "Optisch-aktive Kobaltsalze mit β-Diketonresten im Komplex," *Helv. Chim. Acta* **4**, 113—129.

Lectures (Designated in the text by *L*)

1892 (1) "La stéréochimie de l' azote," in "Conférences de chimie faites au laboratoire de M. Friedel, 1893—94," Georges Carré, Paris **1896**, pp. 60—83; Paris, 1892.

(2) "Kritische Beleuchtung der heutigen Benzoltheorie," Antrittsvorlesung, Eidgenössisches Polytechnikum, Zürich, Summer Semester 1892.

| 1893 | (3) | "Über die Konstitution anorganischer chemischer Verbindungen," Naturforschende Gesellschaft Zürich, June 26. |

1893   (3)   "Über die Konstitution anorganischer chemischer Verbindungen," Naturforschende Gesellschaft Zürich, June 26.

1895   (4)   "Über Molekulargewichtsbestimmungen anorganischer Salze," Schweizerische Naturforschende Gesellschaft, Zermatt, Sept. 9.

1896   (5)   "Lösungsgesetze und einige ihrer Anwendungen," Naturforschende Gesellschaft Zürich, Feb. 3.

        (6)   "Neue Kobaltiake," Schweizerische Naturforschende Gesellschaft, Zürich, September.

1897   (7)   "Über Carbide," Naturforschende Gesellschaft Zürich, Jan. 11.

1898   (8)   "Über Nitroazo-, Azoxy- und Hydrazo-Verbindungen," Schweizerische Naturforschende Gesellschaft, Bern, Aug. 2.

1899   (9)   "Isomerieerscheinungen bei Metallammoniaken," Schweizerische Naturforschende Gesellschaft, Neuchâtel, July 31.

1901   (10)   "Neue chemische Grundstoffe und ihre Stellung im periodischen System," Naturforschende Gesellschaft Zürich, Feb. 11.

        (11)   "Über die Konstitution der Osmiamsäure," Schweizerische Naturforschende Gesellschaft, Zofingen, Aug. 6.

1902   (12)   "Les sels d'ammonium," Schweizerische Naturforschende Gesellschaft, Genève, Sept. 9.

1904   (13)   "Radium und radioaktive Stoffe," *Vierteljahrsschrift der Zürcher Naturforschenden Gesellschaft* 49, 115—127; Zürich, Feb. 15.

        (14)   "Über einige neue Chromsalze," Schweizerische Naturforschende Gesellschaft, Winterthur, Aug. 1.

1905   (15)   "Über Beweglichkeit von Halogen unter dem Einfluss Oxyalkylgruppen," Schweizerische Naturforschende Gesellschaft, Luzern, Sept. 12.

1906   (16)   "Sur les sels hexamminiques stéréo-isomériques," Schweizerische Chemische Gesellschaft, Bern, Feb. 24.

        (17)   "Zur Valenzfrage," *Z. anorg. Chem.* 19, 1345; Verein Deutscher Chemiker, Nürnberg, June 8.

        (18)   "Les phénomènes d'isomérie en chimie inorganique," *Revue générale des sciences pures et appliquées* 17, 538; Paris, 1906.

        (19)   "Über Triamminchromsalze," Schweizerische Naturforschende Gesellschaft, St. Gallen, July 31.

        (20)   "Über neue Fälle von Raumisomerie bei anorganischen Verbindungen," Gesellschaft Deutscher Naturforscher und Ärzte, Stuttgart, Sept. 16.

        (21)   "Untersuchungen über anorganische Konstitutions- und Konfigurations-Fragen," *Ber.* 40, 15—69 (1907); Deutsche Chemische Gesellschaft, Berlin, Nov. 3, 1906.

1907   (22)   "Sur la théorie des bases et de la dissociation électrolytique," Schweizerische Chemische Gesellschaft, Genève, Feb. 16.

        (23)   "Valency," *Chemical News* 96, 128—131; British Association (Section B), Leicester, 1907.

1908   (24)   "Über die essigsauren Salze des Chroms und analoge Verbindungen," Gesellschaft Deutscher Naturforscher und Ärzte, Köln, 1908.

        (25)   "Über Jodopentammin-Kobaltisalze," Schweizerische Naturforschende Gesellschaft, Glarus, Sept. 1.

1909   (26)   "Über mehrkernige Kobaltiake mit vierwertigem Kobalt," Schweizerische Chemische Gesellschaft, Zürich, Mar. 6.

(27) "Konstitutionsbeziehungen und Umwandlungen mehrkerniger Kobaltiake (Relations constitutionelles et transformations des cobaltiaques à plusieurs noyaux)," Schweizerische Naturforschende Gesellschaft, Lausanne, Sept. 7.

1910 (28) "Das Ultramicroscop" (Demonstration), Naturforschende Gesellschaft Zürich, Feb. 21.

(29) "Über die Raumformeln der Kobaltiake," Schweizerische Naturforschende Gesellschaft, Basel, Sept. 6.

1911 (30) "Über den räumlichen Stellungswechsel von Atomen und Atomgruppen bei Umsatz von anorganischen Stereoisomeren," Schweizerische Chemische Gesellschaft, Fribourg, Feb. 25.

(31) "Theorie der Valenz," Z. Elektrochem. 17, 601—609; Deutsche Bunsen-Gesellschaft für angewandte physikalische Chemie, Kiel, May 25.

(32) "Über spiegelbildisomere Metallverbindungen," Karlsruhe, 1911.

(33) "Über optisch-aktive Kobaltverbindungen," Zürcher Chemische Gesellschaft, July, Schweizerische Naturforschende Gesellschaft, Solothurn, Aug. 1.

1912 (34) "Über neue optisch-isomere Metallverbindungen," Schweizerische Chemische Gesellschaft, Basel, March 2.

(35) "Sur les composés métalliques à dissymétrie moléculaire," Bull. Soc. Chim. France [4] 11, No. 14, I—XXIV; Société Chimique de France, Paris, May 24; Am. Chem. J. 48, 314—336.

(36) "Über Verbindungen mit zwei asymmetrischen Kobaltatomen," Verein Deutscher Chemiker, Freiburg im Breisgau, May 29.

(37) Fackelzugrede, talk delivered from balcony of Freiestrasse 111, Zürich on occasion of torchlight procession (Fackelzug) held in honor of the awarding of the Nobel Prize to Werner, Nov. 24 (available as typed manuscript only).

1913 (38) Lecture on Coordination Compounds (Title Unknown), Dansk Kemisk Forening, Copenhagen, Dec. 6.

(39) "Über die Konstitution und Konfiguration von Verbindungen höherer Ordnung, Nobel-Vortrag am 11. Dezember 1913 zu Stockholm gehalten," in "Les Prix Nobel en 1913," P.-A. Norstedt & Fils, Imprimerie Royale, Stockholm 1914, 15 pp.; (a) Naturwissenschaften 2, 1—7 (1914); (b) Verlag von Julius Springer, Berlin 1914, 21 pp.; (c) "Sur la constitution et la configuration des combinaisons d'ordre élevé, conférence faite à l'occasion de la réception du prix Nobel, le 11 décembre 1913," Editions de la Revue Politique et Littéraire et de la Revue Scientifique, Paris, n. d. [1914], 26 pp.; (d) J. chim. phys. 12, 133—152 (1914); (e) "On the Constitution and Configuration of Compounds of Higher Order," in "Nobel Lectures in Chemistry, 1901—1921," edited by the Nobel Foundation, Stockholm, Elsevier Publ. Co., Amsterdam, London, New York 1966; (f) Reviews: (1) J. Am. Chem. Soc. 36, 1324 (1914); (2) Chem. News 109 (Apr. 17, 1914); (3) Tonindustrie-Zeitung 38, No. 32 (1914); (4) Zeitschrift für physikalischen und chemischen Unterricht, No. 5 (1914); (5) Der Seifenfabrikant 34, No. 9 (1914); (6) Chemische Revue über die Fett- und Harz-Industrie 20, No. 4 (1914); (7) Z. Elektrochem. 20, 234 (1914); (8) Z. angew. Chem. 28, 5 (1915); (9) Die Chemische Industrie 37, No. 11 (1914); (10) Physikalische Zeitschrift 16, No. 15 (1914); (11) Z. physik. Chem. 88, 384 (1914).

1914 (40) "Die neuesten Forschungen auf dem Gebiete der optisch aktiven, stickstofffreien, anorganischen Komplexsalze," Chemiker-Zeitung 38, 793.

(41) "Reden von Herrn Prof. Werner" [Acceptance Speech], in "Schweizerische Chemische Gesellschaft: Ansprachen zu Ehren des Herrn Prof. Dr. Werner gehalten bei der Versammlung vom 2. Mai 1914 in Neuenburg," Imprimerie Th. Eberhard, Lausanne 1914, pp. 29—34; Neuchâtel, May 2.

(42) "Neue Ergebnisse der Spaltungsversuche mit anorganischen Verbindungen," *ibid.*, pp. 35—47; *Archives des Sciences physiques et naturelles* 37, 455; Neuchâtel, May 2.

(43) "Über anorganische Konstitutions- und Konfigurationsfragen," Naturforschende Gesellschaft Zürich, June 8.

(44) "Sur l'activité optique de composés chimiques sans carbone," *Compt. rend.* 159, 426—429; Société Chimique de France, Paris, Aug. 17.

1915 (45) "Acides complexes métal-oxaliques et métal-maloniques," Schweizerische Chemische Gesellschaft, Solothurn, Feb. 25.

(46) "Über eine neue Isomerieart bei Kobaltverbindungen und Kobaltverbindungen mit asymmetrischem Kobalt und Kohlenstoff," Schweizerische Naturforschende Gesellschaft, Genève, Sept. 14.

Review Articles (Designated in the text by *R*)

1898 (1) "Stereochemistry among Inorganic Substances," Appendix in "The Arrangement of Atoms in Space," by J. H. van't Hoff, translated by A. Eiloart, Longmans, Green & Co., London, New York 1898, pp. 185—199.

1901 (2) "Der Stand der Chemie am Beginne des XX. Jahrhunderts: Die theoretischen Bestrebungen auf organischem Gebiete," *Chemische Zeitschrift* 1, 1—5, 25—30.

1902 (3) "Unsere Kenntnisse über Konstitution und Synthese der Alkaloïde bis Juni 1902," *Chemische Zeitschrift* 2, 3—7, 42—46, 77—80, 109—112, 139—143, 171—174.

(4) "Die neueren Forschungen auf organischem Gebiete," *Chemische Zeitschrift* 2, No. 8.

(5) "Die neueren Forschungen auf organischem Gebiete bis Ende Februar 1902," *Chemische Zeitschrift* 2, No. 16.

(6) "Über die Fortschritte in der strukturellen Formulierung organischer Verbindungen (bis Ende 1902)," *Chemische Zeitschrift* 2, 300—303, 333—335.

(7) "Organische Chemie, Fortschritte in der Chemie der Zucker," *Chemische Zeitschrift* 2, 493—495, 525—527, 595—597, 633—635.

1903 (8) (With P. Pfeiffer) "Anorganische Chemie," in "Jahrbuch der Chemie," edited by Richard Meyer, Druck von Friedrich Vieweg und Sohn, Braunschweig 1903, XII. Jahrgang (1902), pp. 61—118.

(9) "Fortschritte in der Chemie der metallorganischen Verbindungen der Magnesiumgruppe," *Chemische Zeitschrift* 3, 4—8, 34—38.

(10) "Verbindungen des Pyridins mit Metallsalzen," in "Roscoe-Schorlemmer's Lehrbuch der Chemie (Organische Chemie)," Druck und Verlag von Friedrich Vieweg und Sohn, Braunschweig 1903, pp. 114—137.

1904 (11) (With P. Pfeiffer) "Anorganische Chemie," in "Jahrbuch der Chemie," edited by Richard Meyer, Druck von Friedrich Vieweg und Sohn, Braunschweig 1904, XIII. Jahrgang (1903), pp. 57—119.

(12) (With P. Pfeiffer) "Konstitution und Synthese natürlicher Farbstoffe," *Chemische Zeitschrift* 3, 323—327, 355—359, 388—392, 420—424.

(13) (With P. Pfeiffer) "Organische Chemie," *Chemische Zeitschrift* **3**, 585—587; "I. Fortschritte in der Chemie der Terpene bis Ende Mai 1904," 607—609; "II. Fortschritte auf dem Gebiet der Alkaloide bis Ende Mai 1904," 629—634; "III. Fortschritte in der Chemie der Kohlenhydrate bis Ende Mai 1904," 653—654; "IV. Fortschritte in der Stereochemie bis Ende Mai 1904," 677—682; "V. Fortschritte auf theoretischem Gebiete bis Mai 1904," 705—708, 729—732.

(14) "Radium und radioaktive Stoffe," *Schweiz. Lehrerzeitung* **50**, No. 28, 1—10.

1905 (15) (With P. Pfeiffer) "Anorganische Chemie," in "Jahrbuch der Chemie," edited by Richard Meyer, Druck von Friedrich Vieweg und Sohn, Braunschweig **1905**, XIV. Jahrgang (1904), pp. 65—118.

(16) "Über die Chemie der Pseudophenole und ihrer Derivate," *Chemische Zeitschrift* **5**, 1—5, 51—55.

Texts (Designated in the text by *T*)

(1) "Lehrbuch der Stereochemie," Verlag von Gustav Fischer, Jena 1904; Reviews: (a) *Allgem. Chemiker-Zeitung* **28** (June 24, 1904); (b) *Allgem. Österr. Chemiker und Techniker Zeitung* **7**, No. 17 (Sept. 1, 1904); (c) *Physikalische Zeitschrift* **6**, No. 18 (Sept. 15, 1904); (d) *Schweizerische Wochenschrift für Chemie und Pharmazie* **42** (Oct. 8, 1904); (e) *Deutsche Medizinal-Zeitung* **26**, No. 4 (1905); (f) *Chemische Zeitschrift* **5**, No. 2 (Jan. 15, 1905); (g) *Z. physik. Chem.* **50**, 253 (1905); (h) *Naturwissenschaftliche Rundschau* **20**, 115 (1905); (i) *Z. angew. Chemie* **18**, 1803 (1905).

(2) "Neuere Anschauungen auf dem Gebiete der anorganischen Chemie," Druck und Verlag von Friedrich Vieweg und Sohn, Braunschweig **1905**; Reviews: (1) *Chemiker-Zeitung* **29**, 1093 (1905); (2) *Archives des Sciences physiques et naturelles* **21**, 230 (1906); (3) *Z. angew. Chem.* **19**, 1949 (1906); (4) *Z. Elektrochem.* **8**, 139 (1906); (a) 2nd edition 1909; (b) "New Ideas on Inorganic Chemistry," transl. from 2nd German edition by E. P. Hedley, Longmans, Green & Co., London **1911**; Review: (1) *Chemiker-Zeitung* **32**, 441 (1909); (c) 3rd edition **1913**; Reviews: (1) *Z. angew. Chem.* **27**, 157 (1914); (2) *Wissenschaften* **2**, 139 (1914); (3) *Z. Elektrochem.* **20**, 143 (1914); (4) *Z. physik. Chem.* **87**, 126 (1914); (d) 4th edition, ed. by P. Karrer **1920**; Reviews: (1) *Z. Elektrochem.* **26**, 399 (1920); (2) *Z. physik. Chem.* **96**, 252 (1920); (e) 5th edition, ed. by P. Pfeiffer **1923**; Review: (1) *Z. physik. Chem.* **108**, 432 (1924).

Memberships and Honors

Société Chimique de Paris	Resident Member	Feb. 3, 1892
Naturforschende Gesellschaft Zürich	Member (Secretary 1894-1899; Questor and Vice-President 1904-1906; President 1906-1908; Beisitzer 1908-1910)	Dec. 5, 1892
Schweizerische Naturforschende Gesellschaft	Member	Aug. 1, 1894
"An important German university" *	Call (Berufung)	1895
Universität Bern	Call (Berufung)	Mar., 1897

* Universität Zürich, Rektorats-Archiv, Aktenverzeichnis, Mappe Nr. 140 A/7, Protokoll-Regierungsrat 8. VI. 1895, 973.

Universität Wien	Call (Berufung)	Feb. 10, 1900
Schweizerische Chemische Gesellschaft	Co-Founder; President 1901-1903	Founded Aug. 6, 1901
Universität Basel	Call (Berufung)	June 17, 1902
Deutsche Chemische Gesellschaft	Board Member	Dec., 1902
Gesellschaft Deutscher Naturforschender und Ärzte	Member	Date unknown
Association des étudiants alsaciens-lorrains	Honorary Member	May, 1904
Eidgenössisches Polytechnikum, Zürich	Inquiry as to availability to succeed Prof. E. Bamberger	1905
Königliche Gesellschaft der Naturwissenschaften zu Göttingen	Corresponding Member (Mathematisch-physikalische Classe)	July 20, 1907
Verein Deutscher Chemiker	Member	1908
Republique Française (Ministère de l'Instruction publique et des Beaux-Arts)	Officier de l'Instruction publique	Mar. 15, 1909
Université de Genève	Docteur ès Sciences Physiques, honoris causa	July 9, 1909
Universität Würzburg	Call (Berufung)	June or July, 1910
Société de Physique et d'Histoire Naturelle de Genève	Honorary Member	Oct. 6, 1910
Universität Leipzig	Proposed as successor to Prof. E. O. Beckmann	1911
Universität Zürich, Student Body	Torchlight Procession (Fackelzug) and Presentation of Scroll as expression of thanks for declining call to Universität Würzburg	March, 1911
Imperatorskoe Obshchestvo Liubitelei Estestvoznaniia, Antropologii i Etnografii ([Russian] Imperial Society of the Friends of Natural Science, Anthropology, and Ethnography)	Permanent Member	Oct. 13, 1911
Physikalischer Verein zu Frankfurt am Main	Honorary Member	Nov. 29, 1911
Deutsche Bunsen-Gesellschaft für angewandte physikalische Chemie	Honorary Member	May 17, 1912
Société Chimique de France	Nicholas Leblanc Medal (See L 35)	May 24, 1912
Société Vaudoise des Sciences Naturelles, Lausanne	Honorary Member	July 12, 1913
The Chemical Society, London	Honorary Fellow	June 5, 1913
Universität Zürich, Student Body	Torchlight Procession (Fackelzug) and Wreath of Honor (Ehren-kranz) on occasion of winning the Nobel Prize in chemistry	Nov. 24, 1913

Erziehungswesen des Kantons Zürich	Dankschrift for Nobel Prize	Nov. 15, 1913
Universität Zürich, Philosophische Fakultät, II. Sektion	Dankschrift for Nobel Prize	Nov. 22, 1913
Nobel Foundation, Stockholm	Nobel Prize in chemistry for 1913 (See *L 39*)	Dec. 11, 1913
Deutsche Chemische Gesellschaft	Member	1914
Société Industrielle de Mulhouse	Grande Medaille d'Honneur	Awarded Apr. 29, 1914; Presented Mar. 31, 1915
Eidgenössische Technische Hochschule, Zürich	Doktor der Technischen Wissenschaften, honoris causa (At dedication of new building, Universität Zürich)	Apr. 18, 1914
Schweizerische Chemische Gesellschaft	Werner Plaque by James Vibert (Presented at Neuchâtel Meeting in Werner's Honor; See *L 41* and *L 42*)	May 2, 1914
Schweizerische Chemische Gesellschaft	Establishment at Solothurn meeting of Werner Fund (Fonds Werner) and Werner Prize (Prix Werner)	Feb. 27, 1915
American Chemical Society	Honorary Member	Aug. 1, 1915
Physikalisch-Technische Reichsanstalt, Berlin	Permanent Member	[Nov.?], 1915
Schachgesellschaft Zürich	Honorary Member	Mar. 4, 1916
Academy of Natural Sciences, Philadelphia	Honorary Member	Dec., 1916
Naturforschende Gesellschaft in Basel	Honorary Member	June 13, 1917
Chemical Society of Japan	Werner Memorial Meetings	Held irregularly on Werner's birthday since Dec. 12, 1947
Dr. Emil Bindschedler Fund in memory of Prof. Dr. Alfred Werner		Sept. 9, 1954
Société Chimique de France	Centenaire de Werner (Assemblée Générale Annuelle), Mulhouse	May 26—28, 1966
Swiss Chemical Society (organizer); Swiss Society of Chemical Industries and the International Union of Pure and Applied Chemistry (sponsors)	Alfred Werner Centenary Celebration, Zürich	Sept. 3, 1966
American Chemical Society	Alfred Werner Centennial Symposium, New York	Sept. 11—16, 1966

Index

Herstellung: Konrad Triltsch, Graphischer Betrieb, Würzburg